EXPERIMENTAL CHEMISTRY

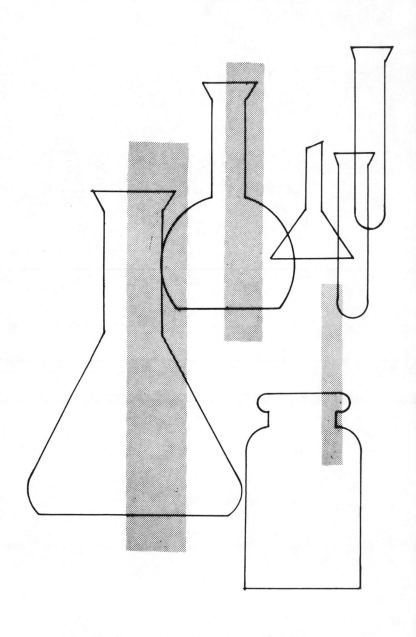

A SENTINEL BOOK

EXPERIMENTAL CHEMISTRY

Nathan Feifer

Associate Professor Physical Science
California State University   San Francisco

ARCO PUBLISHING COMPANY, INC.
219 Park Avenue South, New York, N.Y. 10003

ACKNOWLEDGMENTS:

Photos by Kagan Art Studio, Inc., Brooklyn, N.Y.

Models appearing in photos: Edward Buonomo, John MacKenzie and Robert Spindel.

Drawings by Herbert Ascher.

Revised Edition

First Arco Printing, 1975

Published by Arco Publishing Company, Inc.
219 Park Avenue South, New York, N.Y. 10003
Formerly titled: Let's Explore Chemistry

Library of Congress Catalog Card Number 74-32563
ISBN 0-668-03240-5

Printed in the United States of America

CONTENTS

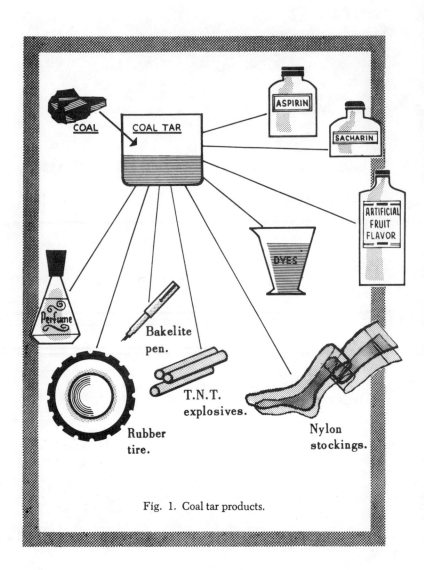

Fig. 1. Coal tar products.

1 - We open the door to
the magic world of chemistry.

HERE is a strange and wonderful world of magic — not mere tricks where the hand is quicker than the eye, but one in which unbelievable marvels are really performed. Chemistry changes rocks to precious metals, charcoal into priceless gems, sawdust into the finest fabrics, and coal into the most valuable of drugs.

We are going to explore this strange world — a world full of surprises and adventures, adventures in chemistry. We will see how the chemist creates this real world of magic, and we will perform our own experiments to see for ourselves how this magic is done.

Most of the experiments described in this book can be performed with ordinary household materials right in your own kitchen. On the other hand, if you enjoy working with more elaborate apparatus you will find many opportunities here.

Every experiment in this book has been selected with careful consideration for your safety. You will learn basic principles of chemistry as you perform each experiment.

What is Chemistry?

Now, before you begin experimenting, there is an important question to be answered. *What is chemistry really about?* The answer may be found by thinking of one of the remarkable achievements of modern science, making coal tar products. Years ago coal had a single use — fuel. Today, coal has very many uses. The chemist has extracted a tar from coal. This coal tar is changed into the many products shown in Fig. 1.

The science of chemistry deals with the knowledge that is needed to make such changes as transforming coal into aspirin.

What does this knowledge consist of? First, the chemist must know:

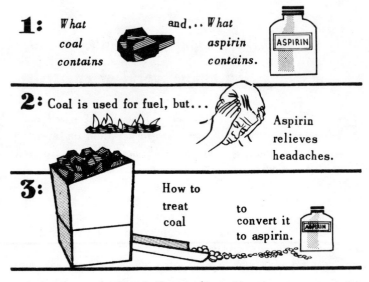

Fig. 2. From coal to aspirin.

How, then, can we describe the science of chemistry? It is the study of: (1) *the composition of matter* (the ingredients present in materials), (2) *the properties of matter* (those qualities by which we recognize materials. Coal is black and it burns, but aspirin is white and it relieves headaches), (3) *the changes in composition of matter* (transforming one kind of material like coal into another material, aspirin).

The transforming of materials is as old as history. In the Middle Ages, men called alchemists tried to change lead into gold, hoping, thereby, to become rich. The alchemists failed because they did not know enough about the composition of matter.

Elements

Although the study of *the composition of matter* is especially important to the chemist, everyone knows something about this topic. A baker, for example, knows the composition of

10

cake. The chemist, however, goes much farther than the baker in studying the cake ingredients, as shown in Fig. 3 below.

What the baker knows –
Cake is made up of the following ingredients:

What the chemist knows –
These ingredients can be broken down to the simplest substances:

FLOUR xxx	Starch and gluten. ⟶	Oxygen, hydrogen, carbon, nitrogen.
	Sugar ⟶	Carbon, hydrogen, oxygen.
S	Salt ⟶	Sodium, chlorine.
	Water ⟶	Hydrogen, oxygen.
EGGS	Eggs ⟶	Oxygen, carbon, hydrogen, sulfur, nitrogen, phosphorus.
BAKING POWDER	Baking powder. ⟶	Sodium, hydrogen, carbon, potassium and oxygen.
MILK	Milk ⟶	Calcium, hydrogen, oxygen, carbon, nitrogen, phosphorous.

Hydrogen, oxygen, nitrogen, carbon, sodium, chlorine, sulfur, phosphorus and calcium are truly simple substances. None of these can be broken down into other materials by chemical means.

11

These simple substances are called *elements*. About 100 such elements are known today. Here is a list of some of the most common elements together with their symbols or chemical abbreviations:

Aluminum (Al)	Cobalt (Co)	Lead (Pb)	Phosphorus (P)
Arsenic (As)	Copper (Cu)	Magnesium (Mg)	Potassium (K)
Boron (B)	Fluorine (F)	Manganese (Mn)	Silver (Ag)
Calcium (Ca)	Gold (Au)	Mercury (Hg)	Sodium (Na)
Carbon (C)	Hydrogen (H)	Neon (Ne)	Sulfur (S)
Chlorine (Cl)	Iodine (I)	Nitrogen (N)	Uranium (U)
Chromium (Cr)	Iron (Fe)	Oxygen (O)	Zinc (Zn)

Compounds

Now, when 2 or more elements are combined they form a *compound*. Water is a compound because it is a combination of the elements hydrogen and oxygen. Similarly, salt and sugar are each compounds. Our world contains many thousands of compounds. Each is a combination of 2 or more elements.

Here is an easy way to form a compound. For our first experiment, we will combine the element silver with the element sulfur.

Chemicals and equipment mentioned in this book can be purchased from your local chemical supply house, model and hobby shop, or from any of the laboratory supply houses listed on page 128. Some will be found right in your own home.

Place a very small pinch of powdered sulfur on a silver coin (a dime or a quarter will do). Spread the sulfur out thinly, and place the coin, sulfur side up, into a pan (Fig. 4). Heat the pan and its contents on your kitchen stove for 30 seconds. Watch the color change. A jet black spot appears on the coin (Fig. 5). This black stuff is a compound of silver and sulfur. The chemist calls this compound silver sulfide. It was formed by combining the elements silver and sulfur. When silverware comes in contact with food containing sulfur (such as eggs), the silverware turns dark. This happens because the silver (in the silverware) combines with the sulfur (in the food) to form the black compound, silver sulfide.

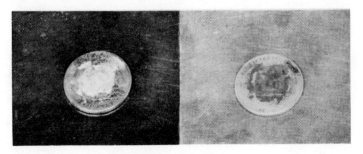

Fig. 4.   From element to compound.   Fig. 5.

Notice that the compound silver sulfide has no resemblance to the elements it contains. The color of the compound, for example, is black, but the elements it contains were silvery and yellow, respectively. *Whenever elements form a compound, they are chemically combined and each element loses its original identity.*

Would you like to make more compounds? Try these:

1. Make copper sulfide by placing a tiny amount of sulfur on a piece of copper (a penny will do) and heat in a pan as before. The red-brown copper combines with the yellow sulfur to form copper sulfide, a black compound.

2. Make silver iodide by smearing iodine (from your medicine cabinet) on a silver coin and heat as before. Silver iodide is a yellow compound. It is used in making high-speed photographic film. Rainmakers have dropped powdered silver iodide into clouds from airplanes, to make artificial rain.

3. Make copper iodide by smearing a penny with iodine and heating as before. Copper iodide is a white compound.

We have taken our first steps into the mysterious world of chemistry. We have learned a little of what chemistry is about and we are now ready to begin experimenting in earnest.

13

2 - Solving the mystery of fire.

FIRE has always had a strange fascination for man. There is something mysterious about the way flames emerge from a burning log of wood and gradually cause it to disappear until only the ashes are left. Even scientists were puzzled by this transformation of solid matter into apparent nothingness. They asked: "Can something really be changed into nothing?" Long debates were held and many experiments were performed until this secret of nature was unlocked.

What Really Happens to a Material When It Burns?

Here are experiments which will help you solve one of the great riddles of all time.

Take two pads of steel wool *(without soap)*. Put one pad aside and roll the other between the palms of your hands into a very small ball. Pierce the ball with a picnic fork or a kitchen fork with a long handle. Then, hold the ball over a kitchen stove flame as shown in Fig. 6.

Soon, the steel wool begins to glow where it touches the flame. Remove it from the flame and *immediately* blow hard on the steel wool. What happens? The steel wool begins to burn brilliantly and a bright glow spreads through the ball (Fig. 7). Continue to blow on it until the glow disappears. Allow the steel wool to cool off completely and then examine it. Compare its color with that of the unheated pad you set aside at the beginning of the experiment.

What difference do you see? The unheated steel wool is a gray color while the heated steel wool is dark blue-black.

Why the change in color? Antoine Lavoisier, the great French chemist first discovered the scientific principle to explain this change, in 1774. He declared that a *burning substance unites with oxygen in the air to form a compound with oxygen.*

14

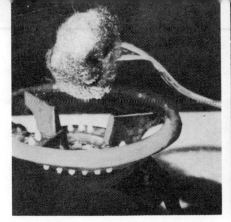 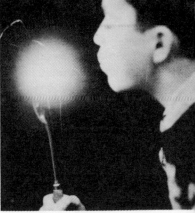

Fig. 6.   Burning steel wool.   Fig. 7.

How does this principle apply to our experiment? Steel wool is an almost pure (99.9%) form of the element iron. When it was heated, the iron actually began to burn. In the burning process, the element iron combined with the element oxygen from the air, and formed a compound. This compound is called *iron oxide*. While the original iron (or steel wool) was grey, the compound iron oxide is blue-black.

Does Burning Affect the Weight?

This experiment raises an interesting question: Does the steel wool weigh more before or after it burns? If our reasoning is correct, the steel wool should be heavier after burning. The steel wool is merely iron, and the added oxygen should

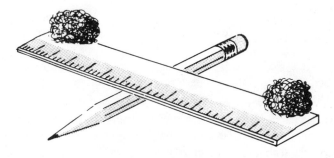

Fig. 8. Burning increases weight.

15

increase the weight after burning. Can we prove this by an experiment? Easily! If you have no weighing apparatus, you can make a simple lever type of balance with a ruler and flat-sided pencil, and use it as shown in Fig. 8.

Place a 12-inch ruler flat on a table. Then slip a flat-sided pencil under the ruler along the 6-inch line and try to balance the ruler like a see-saw, so that neither end touches the table. (The experiment can be done successfully even if you cannot balance the ruler perfectly.)

Next, prepare 2 small compact steel wool balls. Place one ball with its center exactly over the 11-inch mark of the ruler, and the other exactly over the 1-inch mark. The end of the ruler with the heavier ball will move downward, and the end with the lighter ball upward. Cut off tiny amounts of steel wool from the heavier ball, with a scissors, until both balls are balanced or almost balanced. If the steel wool balls cannot be balanced perfectly on the ruler, select the *lighter* one for heating.

Perform the heating operation as described in the previous experiment on page 14. Blow immediately on the heated steel wool on removing it from the flame until it stops burning, but *be careful not to lose any particles by blowing too hard.*

After the steel wool has cooled, replace it on the ruler in its original position.

Now, which steel wool ball is heavier? Of course, the burnt one! This is true of any material that burns. In general, *when a substance burns it unites with oxygen from the air and gains weight.* Now, you may wonder how that can be true of a log of wood or a candle. These obviously disappear when they burn. How can there be a gain in weight? The experiment described in Fig. 9, already performed by chemists, answers this puzzling question.

As the candle burns, the side of the balance with the candle on it becomes *heavier*. The burning candle combines with oxygen from the air to form invisible gases. These gases weigh *more* than the candle, since they are composed of the elements that were in the candle, *plus* oxygen from the air.

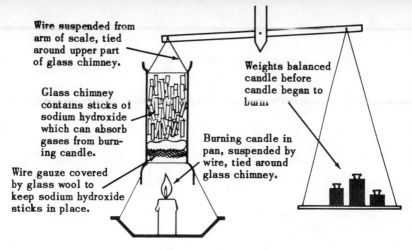

Wire suspended from arm of scale, tied around upper part of glass chimney.

Glass chimney contains sticks of sodium hydroxide which can absorb gases from burning candle.

Wire gauze covered by glass wool to keep sodium hydroxide sticks in place.

Weights balanced candle before candle began to burn.

Burning candle in pan, suspended by wire, tied around glass chimney.

Fig. 9. The candle is no exception to the rule.

We Remove Oxygen from the Air

What percentage of the air is oxygen? The following experiment can help answer this question.

You will need 2 tall drinking glasses (no sloping sides), 1/3 of a steel wood pad, and a pan of water. Wash the steel wool *thoroughly* in soap and water. Without drying it, place it at the bottom of one of the tall glasses. Turn the glass upside down, making sure that the steel wool does not fall out. You may have to spread the steel wool by pulling it apart with your fingers, to make it occupy more space and thus keep its position at the bottom of the glass. Now, set the glass in its inverted (upside down) position into a pan containing a layer of water one inch deep (Fig. 10). Place a second *empty* glass in an inverted position alongside the first glass. The second glass will be used to make comparisons. Observe that no water enters either glass. This is to be expected because the "empty" space in each glass is really filled with air. Now allow your apparatus to remain undisturbed for 72 hours.

When you re-examine the apparatus (Fig. 11), you will see that water has risen in the glass containing the steel wool, but no water has entered the other glass. Furthermore, the water rose 1/5 the distance up the first glass. Measure the distance with a ruler and convince yourself! No matter how often this experiment is repeated, and no matter how large or small the

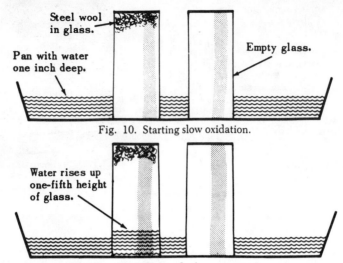

Steel wool in glass.

Empty glass.

Pan with water one inch deep.

Fig. 10. Starting slow oxidation.

Water rises up one-fifth height of glass.

Fig. 11. What made the water rise?

glass, the water always rises 1/5 the distance. The explanation for these results can be found in the fact that air contains 1/5 oxygen (the exact amount is 21%). The steel wool removed the oxygen from the air, and pressure from the outside forced water into the glass.

Slow Oxidation

Do you know how steel wool removed oxygen from the air in this experiment? Examine the steel wool, and you will discover rust spots on it. Chemically speaking, rust is a form of iron oxide. It was produced by the slow combining of the iron in the steel wool with oxygen from the surrounding air. This slow combination of a material with oxygen is called *slow oxidation*. In the first experiment on page 14 we *burned* steel wool. Burning is an example of *rapid* oxidation. Rapid oxidation is generally accompanied by noticeable heat and light in the form of flames. In slow oxidation, heat is liberated very gradually and may be unnoticed.

Have you ever seen an oxy-acetylene torch? This remarkable device produces a flame having a temperature of 3500° Centigrade. It cuts right through iron and steel. How is this

18

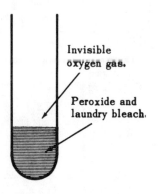

Invisible oxygen gas.

Peroxide and laundry bleach.

Fig. 12. Producing oxygen.

Fig. 13. Testing for oxygen.

possible? The answer lies in the use of *pure* oxygen to support the combustion (burning) of a fuel like acetylene. Ordinarily, fuels combine with the oxygen present in the air, but the air is only 21% oxygen. Pure oxygen hastens the speed of burning and a much hotter flame is produced.

We Make Pure Oxygen

You can perform several striking experiments with pure oxygen obtained from household materials. All you need is some laundry bleach containing sodium hypochlorite (such as clorox) and a bottle of 3% hydrogen peroxide solution (commonly called "peroxide").

Use a 4-inch test tube or a cylindrical pill bottle about 3 inches long, having a diameter not more than one inch. In addition, roll a piece of bathroom tissue paper into the shape of a pencil.

Now fill the test tube (or the pill bottle) 1/4 with hydrogen peroxide. Add a few drops of the laundry bleach, full strength. Notice how vigorously it begins to fizz. This is due to the liberation of pure oxygen from the peroxide. The oxygen now occupies the space above the liquid in your test tube (Fig. 12). Cover the tube with a cardboard to keep the oxygen from escaping, and put it into the test tube rack while you prepare a test for oxygen as follows:

Ignite one end of the rolled tissue paper with a match. Allow

19

see Page 37

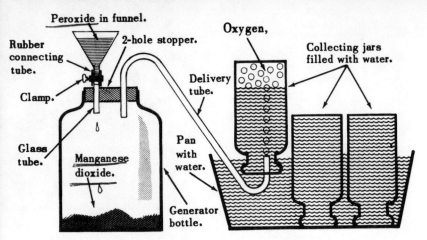

Fig. 14. Preparing pure oxygen.

the tissue to burn for one or two seconds. Then blow the flame out but permit several sparks to remain glowing. Place the glowing portion of the paper into the oxygen you have prepared. If the paper is still glowing when it is placed into the oxygen, you will be pleased with the result. In less than a second, the glow brightens and the paper bursts into flames (Fig. 13). This reaction is a test for oxygen.

The experiment you have just performed proves that materials burn at a faster rate in pure oxygen than they can burn in the air around us. Therefore, spectacular effects can be produced by using pure oxygen. If you want to prepare this gas in larger quantities, and see these spectacular effects, obtain and set up the materials and apparatus shown in Fig. 14. To obtain manganese dioxide, open an old flashlight dry cell. The black *powder* is manganese dioxide. Save the carbon rod for another experiment. After the apparatus is set up, proceed as follows:

1. Add the peroxide to the manganese dioxide by opening the clamp and allowing the liquid to pass through the funnel *a few drops at a time.*

2. Allow the first portion of gas coming through the delivery tube (about 12 bubbles) to escape into the air. This gas is impure since it is a mixture of oxygen you have prepared and air already present in the generator.

3. Then hold the first collecting jar over the delivery tube and allow the gas from the generator to enter the collecting jar. You know the jar is full of gas when all of the water it contains is displaced. Repeat the same process with the other two jars.

4. To avoid losing the gas as the jars are removed from the pan, cover the mouth of the jar with a stiff card or a glass plate *before* removing the jar from the water (Fig. 15). Then set the covered jar right side up on the table (Fig. 16).

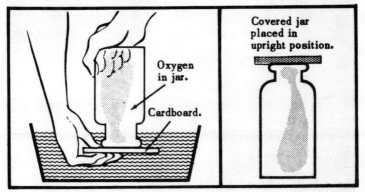

Fig. 15.   Storing pure oxygen.   Fig. 16.

You are now ready to perform several experiments with oxygen. Use one jar of the gas to test for oxygen, as described on page 19. You may perform this test several times with the same jar of oxygen before the gas is used up. Try a wood splint instead of the tissue. (The common test for oxygen is to make a glowing wood splint burst into flames.)

A second jar of oxygen may be used to compare the burning of a candle in oxygen with its burning in air. Wind the end of a wire (or hairpin) around a very small candle and ignite the candle. Then lower the candle into the jar of oxygen (see Fig. 17). Notice how brilliantly the candle burns in pure oxygen. Will this brilliance last indefinitely? Let the flame burn for a little while and see what happens. Can you explain the result?

Use a third jar of oxygen to compare the burning of steel

21

L-shaped steel wool.

Fig. 17. Candle burning in oxygen.

Fig. 18.

Fig. 19. Burning steel wool in oxygen.

wool in air and in pure oxygen. Roll a piece of steel wool into the shape of a pencil about 6 inches long. Then make a right angle bend in the steel wool, at a point about 1/3 from one of its ends (Fig. 18). Hold the short end of the bend and heat the opposite end in a gas flame just long enough to make it glow. Then plunge the glowing end of the steel wool into the jar of oxygen (Fig. 19). Notice how the steel begins to sparkle. Some of the steel may even melt as a result of the great heat produced by its burning in pure oxygen. *Oxygen allows other materials* (like wood, wax and iron) *to burn. We say oxygen supports combustion.*

How to Use a Bunsen Burner

A Bunsen burner requires oxygen from the air. It is designed to produce different types of flames. (Almost every experiment in this book can be performed with an alcohol lamp or a kitchen gas stove. In a few experiments, a Bunsen burner will be recommended.) Before we use the Bunsen burner, let's study the diagram in Fig. 20 and find out how it works.

To light the Bunsen burner, first close the air inlet (the air inlet can be made smaller or larger by turning the collar). Strike a match about a foot away from the burner, turn the gas on full, and bring the lit match to the top of the barrel.

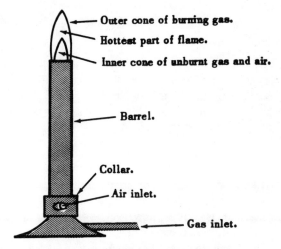

Fig. 20. The Bunsen burner.

This ignites the gas and air mixture which has already entered at the bottom of the barrel. By opening the air inlet, this flame becomes blue. The blue flame is much hotter than the yellow flame. The blue flame has distinct cones as shown in Fig. 20. However, the inner cone of the blue flame consists of unburnt gas and is quite cold. The outer cone (directly above the inner cone) consists of very hot burning gas. Reduce the amount of gas until the flame is about 2 1/2 inches high.

Caution: If too much air enters the barrel through the air inlet, the flame descends to the bottom of the barrel and continues to burn with a loud hissing or whistling sound. This is called "striking back." It may heat the burner enough to melt the rubber hose, and burn the person holding the burner. When the flame "strikes back," do the following: (1) Shut off the gas immediately, (2) allow the burner to cool if it is too hot, (3) close the air inlet. Then relight the gas but do not open the air inlet too much.

3 - Working wonders with water.

W ATER, water, everywhere but not a drop to drink."
When the poet, Coleridge, wrote this line he was thinking of the ocean. He never dreamt the time would come when
it would be possible to change the saltiest sea water into perfectly pure water. Let me tell you how to do this.

We Purify Water

First, let us see what happens to a material like salt when
it mixes with water. Place a level teaspoonful of salt in a large
glass of water and stir with a spoon until all of the salt has
dissolved. No salt is visible now, yet, you know that it is
present in the water. A mixture like this, in which all of the
solid material seems to have disappeared, is called a *solution*.
The chemist believes that the solid salt has been separated
into very minute particles, too small to be seen by the most
powerful microscope. These particles are scattered evenly
throughout the water and they will not settle to the bottom
of the glass no matter how long the solution stands. If you
want to separate the salt and the water, however, do the
following: Pour the salt water into a pan and heat to boiling.
Hold a second *dry, clean* saucepan over the boiling salt water
for 1/2 minute, to catch the steam that is escaping (Fig. 21).
Remove the *second* pan from above the boiling water and examine its contents. You will see that some of the steam has
condensed to form water. Allow this water to cool; then pour
a few drops into a clean spoon and taste it. *Right!* There is
absolutely no trace of salt in this water. Why?

Water, upon reaching a temperature of 212° Fahrenheit,
boils and escapes as steam. At this temperature, nothing happens to the dissolved salt and it remains in the solution. The
escaping steam (which contained no salt) was then cooled by

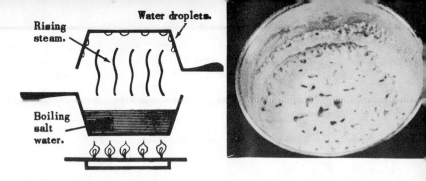

Fig. 21.　　Separating water and salt.　　Fig. 22.

the saucepan above it. This cooling action changed the steam into water, but you now have *pure* water. (In a while, I shall tell you how to obtain large quantities of pure water by this method. Meanwhile, let us continue with this experiment.)

Can we recover all of the salt in the water, in its original dry condition? *Of course!* Continue boiling the salt water until all of the water has been driven off as steam. When the pan is dry examine it and you will find the original salt clinging to the sides and bottom (Fig. 22). Scrape this salt off the pan and you will have the same quantity you started with, namely, one level teaspoonful.

This experiment shows how we may separate a dissolved material (like salt) from the liquid in which it is dissolved (water). The method we used is the basis for the process called *distillation* in which water containing salt and other impurities is converted into pure water. (Even water containing poisonous substances dissolved in it may be made fit to drink by the process of distillation.)

Here is another experiment to illustrate distillation. Set up the apparatus shown in Fig. 23. Be sure that all parts fit snugly: the rubber stopper, the glass tubes and the rubber tubes. Dissolve *one tiny crystal* of potassium permanganate in 1/2 glass of water. Pour the purple solution of potassium permanganate and water into the pyrex flask shown in Fig. 23. Before heating the flask, be sure that it is dry on the outside, otherwise it may crack. Begin heating the flask gently, by moving the burner or alcohol lamp slowly in a circle under the flask, in order to spread the heat.

25

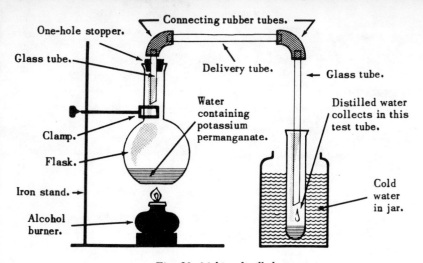

Fig. 23. Making distilled water.

After heating the flask gently for 2 full minutes, the burner may be kept in one position to concentrate the heat and bring the solution to a boil. Continue boiling until you have collected about 1/3 of a test tube of pure water. Then stop heating and use a pot holder to remove the glass tube from the test tube, *immediately*. (This is necessary to prevent the water from being forced back into the flask; also, since the glass tube has become hot, the use of a pot holder is advisable.)

You have just produced *distilled water*. This is very pure and it is used for special purposes such as treating storage batteries or preparing medical solutions to be injected into the blood. Ordinary drinking water, although fit to drink, usually contains enough dissolved material to prevent its use for hypodermic injections or for storage batteries.

Solvents and Solutes

For future reference it will be useful to remember certain chemical terms. A liquid capable of dissolving other materials is called a *solvent*. In the experiments you have performed, the solvent was water. On the other hand, the material that is dissolved by the solvent is called the *solute*. We have used two solutes. The first was salt; the second was potassium permanganate. Finally, a solution is defined as a uniform (evenly distributed) mixture of solute and solvent.

Not all impurities can dissolve in water, but there are other ways of purifying water. Let's prepare a mixture containing undissolved material and then we will purify it. Place half a teaspoon of granulated sugar into a large test tube and an equal amount of starch (cornstarch, not soluble starch) in another test tube. Fill each test tube with warm water. Stopper and shake both tubes vigorously for a full minute. Note that the mixture of sugar and water (Fig. 24A) looks perfectly clear, but the mixture containing starch (Fig. 24B) is quite cloudy. Allow each mixture to stand undisturbed for about 10 minutes and then examine both. You will observe that the starch has begun to settle (Fig. 24C) but the sugar does not.

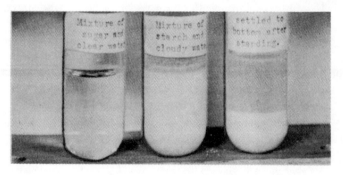

Fig. 24A.   Fig. 24B.   Fig. 24C.

Filtration

There is another difference between the starch mixture and the sugar mixture. This difference is noticeable when we try to pass each mixture through a *filter*. For the next experiment, obtain a funnel and some filter paper. Prepare the filter paper as shown in Fig. 25. Now pour the sugar water through the filter. Taste the water that comes through. Don't feel disappointed if you detect the taste of sugar, for that is exactly what is to be expected. Since the sugar is dissolved, the sugar particles are smaller than the pores in the filter paper, and the sugar passes through the filter. Now, stir up the mixture of starch and water and pour it through another filter. Examine

27

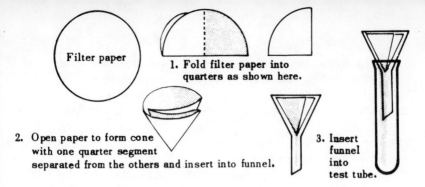

Fig. 25. How to make a filter.

the water that comes through and you will observe that it is perfectly clear. Taste the water and you will find no trace of starch in it. This happened because the particles of starch were too large to pass through the filter paper. Where is the starch? Examine the filter paper and you will find all of the starch there.

This inability of certain materials to pass through a filter is the basis for still another method of purifying water, called *filtration*. Cities have filtration plants in which muddy water is passed through a special filter to produce clear water.

The experiments you have just completed illustrate several important chemical ideas. A substance which can be dissolved is said to be *soluble*. Salt, sugar and potassium permanganate are soluble in water. A substance which cannot be dissolved is said to be *insoluble*. Starch and sand are insoluble in water.

The man who operates a dry cleaning store relies heavily upon chemical knowledge. He specializes in removing stains. To the chemist the removal of stains is often a question of finding the right solvent (the stain remover) for the right solute (the stain). Try this experiment:

How to Remove an Iodine Stain

Smear a *very small amount* of tincture of iodine (from the medicine chest) on the palm of your hand. (Make sure you have no cuts on your palm.) Let the iodine dry thoroughly. Now wash off half of the stain with some paper tissue that has been moistened with water. Then wash the rest of the stain with paper tissue that has been moistened with rubbing alcohol. Notice the difference. The alcohol removes the iodine much more completely because iodine is very soluble in alcohol. The water removes very little iodine because iodine is almost insoluble in water. In other words, alcohol is a good solvent for iodine, but water is not. Remember this when you try to remove an iodine stain.

Saturated Solutions

Every housewife knows that laundry washes better in warm water than in cold water. Why? Because the ability of a solvent, like water, to dissolve a substance generally depends upon the temperature. You can prove this in the following experiment:

Fill 1/4 of a glass with cold water, and add 1/2 a teaspoonful of potassium alum. Stir until the alum dissolves completely. Now keep on adding 1/2 teaspoon portions of alum until no more dissolves even after stirring. You now have a *saturated* solution. A saturated solution is one which has all the solute it can dissolve at a given temperature.

If you raise the water temperature, more alum can be dissolved. Prove this by placing the solution you prepared into an enamel pan and heating until it begins to boil. Now the solution is no longer saturated. Add 4 more teaspoons of alum to the solution and stir. This time you will find that the alum dissolves completely.

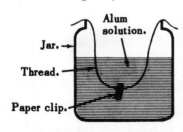

Fig. 26. Growing crystals.   Fig. 27. An alum crystal.*

*Reproduced by special permission from MODERN PHYSICAL SCIENCE by Brooks and Tracey, 1957 edition, Henry Holt and Company, Inc.

We Grow Crystals

The solution you have just prepared can be employed to produce beautifully shaped crystals. Pour the hot alum solution into a jar or beaker. Place a small clip on a thread, and suspend it in the solution as shown in Fig. 26. Now cover the jar and wrap it completely with a thick cloth to prevent the solution from cooling too quickly. Set it aside for about 24 hours without disturbing it. When you examine it again, you will find crystals of alum forming around the thread.

This formation of crystals may be explained as follows: As the solution is cooled, it becomes saturated. Upon further cooling, there is more solute present in the water than can be dissolved. The excess solute comes out of the solution. Because this occurs gradually, the particles of solute are able to arrange themselves in a geometric pattern.

If you enjoyed making crystals, you may wish to grow others. I suggest you try zinc sulfate, chrome alum, potassium sodium tartrate or copper sulfate. In each case the method is the same. Prepare a *hot saturated solution* of the substance and let it cool *very slowly* in a container having a suspended string. (For copper sulfate coat paper clip with wax.) The string acts as a center about which the crystals grow.

After you have grown a large crystal, you can increase its size. Place a single crystal into an open jar filled with a *cold* saturated solution of the same substance, and allow the solution to evaporate for several days. Keep adding more of the cold saturated solution from time to time, to keep the crystal covered. This process may be repeated several times with an increase in the growth of the crystal each time.

Then remove the crystal and preserve it by coating it with a layer of clear nail polish or clear airplane dope.

We Decompose Water

In Chapter I, we mentioned that water is a compound of the elements hydrogen and oxygen. See Fig. 28 for the diagram of an experiment you can perform to prove this. Study the diagram carefully, and then do the following:

1. Prepare a saturated solution (see page 29) of any *one*

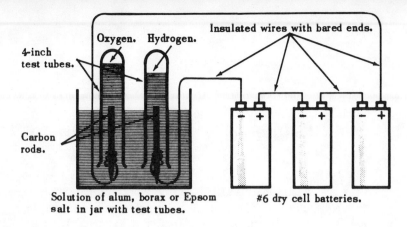

Fig. 28. Decomposing water.

of these common materials: borax, Epsom salt, or potassium alum.

2. The two carbon rods may be purchased or obtained from old flashlight dry cells. See page 20. Connect each rod to a bare end of copper wire. Then cover all of the bare wire that will come into contact with the solution with melted candle wax or other insulation.

3. As the current passes through the solution, notice bubbles of gas form at each electrode (or carbon rod). The gas forming at the electrode connected to the plus pole is oxygen. The gas at the other electrode is hydrogen.

4. To test for hydrogen, hold the test tube with this invisible gas upside down. Hydrogen is lighter than air, and it will escape if the test tube is held right side up. Keep the test tube inverted at all times, and pass it over a lit candle. You will hear a popping sound as the hydrogen catches fire.

5. The test for oxygen may be performed as described on page 19.

As the oxygen and hydrogen are produced, the water volume gradually decreases, but the amount of dissolved material (alum, etc.) remains exactly the same. This proves that the oxygen and hydrogen came only from the water. Consequently, we have shown that water is composed of hydrogen and oxygen.

4 - Understanding the magic in formulas.

WHEN Japan entered World War II, her armies invaded the East Indies and cut off the world's chief supply of quinine. Quinine, one of our most important medicines, is invaluable in the treatment of malaria. It is extracted from the cinchona tree which grows in the East Indies.

For many months our supply of quinine dwindled. Then in 1944 the problem of obtaining this drug was solved. Two American chemists, Robert B. Woodward and William Doering, announced they had made quinine artificially. How did they do it? The answer lies in the magic word *formula.*

There are thousands of substances in our universe known to the chemist. He knows exactly what each contains, and he knows how to make many of them artificially because he knows their formulas. If you wish to increase you knowledge of chemistry, read this chapter carefully as we look into the questions: *What is the meaning of a chemical formula? Why is it so important to the chemist?*

We Translate a Chemical Formula

Let's look at two formulas: H_2O (water) and $C_{12}H_{22}O_{11}$ (cane sugar). The letters in the formulas stand for the elements present in each substance. (These letters are listed as symbols on page 12.) The formula H_2O tells us that water is composed of hydrogen (H) and oxygen (O), and the formula $C_{12}H_{22}O_{11}$ tells us that cane sugar is composed of carbon (C), hydrogen (H), and oxygen (O). The numbers 12, 22, and 11 in the formula for cane sugar, and the number 2 in the formula for water are called *subscripts*. Subscripts have a special meaning for the chemist.

To understand the meaning of the subscripts in a formula, first ask yourself this question: "What is the *smallest* amount of water that can exist?" The answer, of course, is not a drop of water. Even the smallest drop of water visible to the naked eye can be placed under a microscope and can be divided into many smaller drops. These smaller drops would no longer be visible to the naked eye, yet each smaller drop could, in turn, be divided into still smaller droplets of water.

How Small is a Molecule?

If each droplet of water were to be divided in half over and over again, until the particles of water were no more than about 1/100,000,000 of an inch in width, we would then have the smallest units of water than can possibly exist. These tiny units are called molecules of water. *A molecule is the smallest amount of a substance that can exist.*

Every substance is made up of molecules. This is true not only of water, but also of sugar, starch, salt, iron oxide, alcohol, etc., etc.

You can imagine how small a molecule is if an ordinary drop of water contains more than 1,000,000,000,000,000,000,000 water molecules. No one has ever seen an individual water molecule, but its size has been discovered by mathematical calculations based on scientific experiments. Measuring molecules is part of the work of the physical chemist, who uses the science of physics to study chemistry.

The following experiement shows that the molecules of a substance are very, very small indeed. We are going to prove that one molecule of potassium permanganate is smaller than one-millionth of a drop of water.

For this experiment we need a medicine dropper, 2 pint-size jars, a glass stirring rod, a 1/4 - spoon measure, water, and some solid or powdered potassium permanganate (enough to fill the 1/4 - spoon). See Fig. 29. You may have enough potassium permanganate left over from the distillation experiment described on page 25. Dissolve a level 1/4 - spoonful of potassium permanganate in a pint jar of lukewarm water by stirring until all of the solid has disappeared completely. You now have a dark purple solution.

(Caution! Be sure to wash the measuring spoon *thoroughly*

Fig. 29. Getting ready to "measure" molecules.

after you are through using it. *Never* attempt to taste chemical substances no matter how attractive they appear to be!)

Before we go ahead, let's stop and do some figuring. A 1/4-spoon can hold 18 drops of water. (You can check this for yourself with a medicine dropper.) A pint of water contains slightly more than 9,000 drops of water. (If you are very ambitious, you can check this, too.) When you dissolved the permanganate (the equivalent of 18 drops) in the pint of water (the equivalent of 9,000 drops) you produced a solution by spreading the 18 drops of permanganate equally among 9,000 drops of water. Each drop of the solution, therefore, contains 18 ÷ 9,000 of a drop of permanganate. Now 18 ÷ 9,000 equals 1/500. Therefore, each drop of your solution contains 1/500 of a drop of permanganate.

Now, with your medicine dropper, pick up some of this solution and place 9 drops in the other pint jar. Fill the second jar with water and stir thoroughly. Naturally, the second solution is much lighter than the first, but the purple color is quite visible.

Now, how much permanganate is there in a drop of this solution? We took 9 drops, each containing 1/500 of a drop of permanganate, and divided this equally among another 9,000 drops of water in the second jar. Mathematically, then, each drop of the new solution now contains 9 x 1/500 x 1/9,000 of a drop of permanganate, or 1/500,000 of a drop. In other words, each drop of this solution contains the equivalent of 1/500,000 of a drop of permanganate.

Now pour off half of this solution and add enough water to fill the pint jar again. Stir thoroughly. Is the purple color still visible? It should be! Then, each drop of solution now contains half the amount of permanganate as before, namely 1/1,000,000 of a drop!

Repeat the last step by pouring off half of the solution and refilling the pint jar with water. Stir again. You still see a purple tinge. Each drop of solution now contains an amount of permanganate that is even smaller than one-millionth of a drop of water! It contains 1/2,000,000 of a drop.

Each time you pour off half of the solution and add an equivalent amount of water, you cut the quantity of permanganate in half. You know that permanganate is still there as long as you see even the faintest tinge of purple. For best results, place an unlined sheet of white paper under the jar and look downward through the solution to see if any purple is still visible. With care, you will observe some color until you reach about 1/16,000,000 of permanganate in water.

The actual size of the potassium permanganate molecule is much smaller than one-sixteen millionth of a drop of water. But our experiment is not sensitive enough to enable us to detect smaller particles. Smaller particles may often be detected by the use of instruments like the ultramicroscope and the electron microscope. (Your future studies in chemistry will show you that the color and the size of the particles we have described are believed to be due to units called ions rather than molecules; but in this case, the two do not differ much in their dimensions.)

Atoms

Now that we have proof that molecules are very small indeed, let us continue to examine these amazingly little particles. We have learned that water is composed of the elements oxygen and hydrogen. This means that even a single molecule of water contains both oxygen and hydrogen. Scientists have come to the conclusion that a molecule of water contains two particles of the element hydrogen and one particle of the element oxygen. It may be illustrated in the following way:

These unit particles of elements in the molecule are called *atoms*. *An atom is the smallest unit of an element found in a molecule.*

We see, then, that the water molecule contains two atoms of hydrogen and one atom of oxygen. This information is condensed into the formula for water, H_2O. *A chemical formula shows how many and what kind of atoms are in a molecule.* The *subscript* tells us the *number* of atoms and the *symbol* tells us the *kind* of atom in the molecule.

Let's look at some other formulas and see what they mean. The formula for cane sugar is $C_{12}H_{22}O_{11}$. This means that a molecule of sugar is composed of 12 atoms of carbon, 22 atoms of hydrogen and 11 atoms of oxygen. This is a rather large molecule.

Now, let's get back to the quinine shortage problem at the beginning of this chapter. The formula for quinine is $C_{20}H_{24}N_2O_2$. This, too, is a large molecule since it contains 20 carbon atoms, 24 hydrogen atoms, 2 nitrogen atoms and 2 oxygen atoms. It took considerable knowledge and skill to combine all these atoms to produce quinine, but Woodward and Doering found the way.

Formulas are most useful because they help us understand chemical changes (or chemical reactions, as they are often called).

Chemical Equations

In the experiment on page 12 we made silver sulfide from

silver (Ag) and sulfur (S). When these elements were combined, each atom of sulfur united with *two* atoms of silver to form a molecule of silver sulfide. We can picture the reaction between the atoms of these elements as follows:

| 2 atoms of silver | + | one atom of sulfur | yields (or forms) | one molecule of silver sulfide. |

The chemist condenses this picture by writing a *chemical equation:*

$$2\,Ag + S \longrightarrow Ag_2S$$

This chemical equation is read as follows: Two atoms of silver and one atom of sulfur yield (form) one molecule of silver sulfide. (The chemical equation shows us the proportions in which substances react with each other.)

A more complicated chemical reaction you observed was the liberation of oxygen from hydrogen peroxide (see page 19). The formula for hydrogen peroxide is H_2O_2 because its molecule contains 2 hydrogen atoms and 2 oxygen atoms. The formula for oxygen gas is O_2. This means one molecule of oxygen is composed of 2 oxygen atoms. Now, when hydrogen peroxide (H_2O_2) gives off oxygen (O_2), water is formed too. The following change takes place:

| 2 molecules of H_2O_2 (hydrogen peroxide) | yield | 1 molecule of O_2 (oxygen) | + | 2 molecules of H_2O (water) |

The chemist condenses this picture by writing a chemical equation:

$$2\,H_2O_2 \longrightarrow O_2 + 2\,H_2O$$

This is read as follows: Two molecules of H_2O_2 (hydrogen peroxide) yield one molecule of O_2 (oxygen) and two molecules of H_2O (water). In reading the left-hand side of this equation, we must remember that H_2O_2 means one molecule of hydrogen peroxide; consequently, $2\ H_2O_2$ means two molecules of hydrogen peroxide. On the right-hand side of the equation, O_2 stands for one molecule of oxygen which is composed of two atoms of that element. Finally, the $2\ H_2O$ on the extreme right-hand side of the equation stands for two molecules of water.

Our formulas show us that different substances may contain the same elements. For example, water and hydrogen peroxide both contain hydrogen and oxygen. What makes them different substances? Their formulas show us this difference. The formula for water is H_2O, and the formula for hydrogen peroxide is H_2O_2.

Furthermore, when a molecule of H_2O_2 loses some of its oxygen, it becomes H_2O. Consequently, when you apply hydrogen peroxide (H_2O_2) on a cut or wound, it is changed into water (H_2O) as it gives off oxygen. This oxygen kills bacteria.

Formulas are also useful to the chemist because they tell him *how much* material to use in making substances. Let us suppose you wish to make silver chloride without wasting any materials. (Silver chloride is used as a coating on photographic film, and it is too expensive to waste.)

To make silver chloride, you must first know its formula, AgCl. According to this formula, a molecule of silver chloride contains one atom of silver (Ag) and one atom of chlorine (Cl). Now you must know the weights of these atoms.

Using Atomic Weights

In chemistry, we compare the weights of atoms and we call the comparative weight the *atomic weight*. The lightest atoms in the universe are those of the element hydrogen. Therefore, if we say that an atom of hydrogen has *one* unit of weight, an atom of oxygen (which is 16 times as heavy as an atom of hydrogen) has *16* units of weight. By comparing these atoms

38

with an atom of silver, we find that the silver atom has 108 units of weight.

Remember that the atomic weight of an element is the comparative weight of an atom. Here are the atomic weights of several common elements:

Hydrogen (H)	= 1	Phosphorus (P)	=	31
Carbon (C)	= 12	Chlorine (Cl)	=	35
Nitrogen (N)	= 14	Calcium (Ca)	=	40
Oxygen (O)	= 16	Silver (Ag)	=	108
Sodium (Na)	= 23	Lead (Pb)	=	207
Magnesium (Mg)	= 24	Uranium (U)	=	238

Notice that uranium (U) one of the heaviest atoms in the universe, has an atomic weight of 238. This means that an atom of uranium is 238 times as heavy as an atom of hydrogen.

The Law of Definite Proportions

Atomic weights are used to find the proportions of elements needed to make a compound. If you wish to make AgCl, you take note that a molecule of this compound contains one atom of Ag and one atom of Cl. Each atom of silver has an atomic weight of 108 and each atom of chlorine has an atomic weight of 35. In making AgCl you must combine 108 units of weight of silver with 35 units of weight of chlorine. Thus, you can combine 108 pounds of silver with 35 pounds of chlorine or you can combine 108 ounces of silver with 35 ounces of chlorine. No matter which units of weight you use, you must keep the ratio of 108 to 35. If you try to change this ratio, either some silver or some chlorine will remain uncombined. This fact was discovered by the French chemist, Louis Proust, in 1799, and is called the Law of Definite Proportions. This scientific law states that the elements in a compound are always combined in the same unchanging proportion by weight.

39

The Law of Definite Proportions is one of the most important statements in chemistry because it enables the chemist to know exactly how much material he needs to make *any* substance, whether it be silver chloride, soap or sulfa drugs. Let us look at another example showing how this law is used.

Suppose we wish to combine hydrogen and oxygen to form water. The formula for water is H_2O and a molecule of this substance contains two atoms of hydrogen and one atom of oxygen. From our table of atomic weights, we find that the atomic weight of hydrogen is 1. In a molecule of H_2O, however, there are *two* atoms of hydrogen. Thus, both hydrogen (H) atoms have a total atomic weight of 2. The atomic weight of oxygen is 16, and since there is only one oxygen atom in a water molecule, the total atomic weight of the oxygen is still 16.

Therefore, according to the Law of Definite Proportions, 2 units of weight of hydrogen combine with 16 units of weight of oxygen. Consequently, we can unite 2 pounds of hydrogen with 16 pounds of oxygen to form water. What would happen if we tried to unite 3 pounds of hydrogen with 16 pounds of oxygen? Only 2 pounds of hydrogen would unite with the oxygen, and one pound of hydrogen would remain uncombined.

Scientific laws such as The Law of Definite Proportions describe the way in which nature behaves. We cannot change this natural law, but we can take advantage of our knowledge of it in our daily lives, to make synthetics like quinine, silver chloride, hydrogen peroxide and countless other important and useful compounds.

5 - Experimenting with clever carbon.

IN THE year 1775 the great French chemist, Antoine Lavoisier, appeared before a gathering of distinguished scientists and performed a most unusual experiment. He took a diamond and *burned* it.

To the reader, this may seem like a foolish waste of a precious stone. This was no waste, however. Lavoisier's experiment eventually led science to make diamonds *artificially*. Just what did Lavoisier prove? By burning a diamond, he showed this valuable gem was nothing more than a crystallized form of carbon. Think of it! A diamond is nothing more than a different form of carbon, the same carbon found in charcoal, chimney soot or hard coal.

Theoretically, then, it should be possible to change charcoal into diamond. For more than a century many scientists tried to do this, and in 1896 Henri Moissan, another great French chemist, announced that he had succeeded. He dissolved charcoal in molten iron. When the molten iron cooled, he broke it apart and found tiny bits of diamond inside. Others have improved on Moissan's work, but there is still a fortune awaiting anyone who discovers a way of producing really large crystals of this precious gem from charcoal.

Let's go back to Lavoisier's experiment and find out how he proved that diamond was a form of carbon.

When ordinary carbon burns, it unites with oxygen from the air to form carbon dioxide, as shown in this equation:

$$C \quad + \quad O_2 \longrightarrow CO_2$$

(Carbon) + (Oxygen)   (yields)   (Carbon dioxide)

Fig. 30.   Testing for CO_2.   Fig. 31.

(Carbon dioxide is an invisible gas, but its presence can easily be detected as we shall soon see.)

When Lavoisier burned a diamond, he obtained the same result, carbon dioxide. This proved that diamond and carbon are the same chemical element.

We Oxidize Carbon

For our first experiment with carbon, we will show that burning charcoal produces carbon dioxide. We need a stick of charcoal, a small jar (baby food size) and some clear lime-water. See Fig. 30.

Heat one end of the charcoal stick in a gas flame until the stick glows. Remove the stick from the flame and blow on it strongly to make it glow more brightly. Thrust the stick into the empty jar and hold it there until it completely stops glowing. Remove the stick and repeat the process of heating, blowing and placing the glowing stick into the jar 3 more times. Then remove the charcoal from the jar.

The jar now contains the invisible gas carbon dioxide (CO_2). To prove it, add enough limewater to form a layer about 1/2 an inch deep in the jar. Then cover the jar and shake it for about 10 full seconds. Notice that the limewater, which was clear, turns *cloudy* or *milky* in appearance (Fig. 31). Turning clear limewater cloudy is a chemical test for carbon dioxide. Pour a 1/2 - inch layer of limewater into another jar and shake for 10 seconds. Now the limewater does not turn cloudy. Can you explain this?

Now, why does limewater turn cloudy when it comes in contact with CO_2? Let's try to understand the complicated reaction that takes place between these two substances

Limewater is a water solution of calcium hydroxide. A molecule of calcium hydroxide contains the atoms shown in this diagram:

The formula for calcium hydroxide is $Ca(OH)_2$. The parenthesis is used to show that the O (oxygen) atom and the H (hydrogen) atom are held together to each other more firmly than they are held to the atom of Ca (calcium). The (OH) in the formula is called the *hydroxide radical*, and $(OH)_2$ means there are 2 hydroxide radicals in the molecule. A radical is any group of atoms in a molecule that tend to stay together.

When limewater is added to carbon dioxide, the following reaction takes place:

$$Ca(OH)_2 \ + \ CO_2 \longrightarrow CaCO_3 \ + \ H_2O$$

$Ca(OH)_2$	+	CO_2	yield	$CaCO_3$	+	H_2O
(calcium hydroxide)		(carbon dioxide)		(calcium carbonate)		(water)

In the above equation, one molecule of calcium hydroxide, $Ca(OH)_2$, reacts with one molecule of carbon dioxide (CO_2), to form one molecule of calcium carbonate $(CaCO_3)$

43

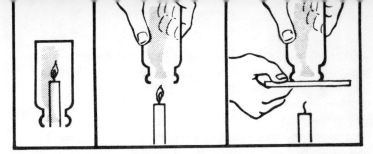

Fig. 32.   Fig. 33.   Fig. 34.
What does a burning candle produce?

and one molecule of water (H_2O). The calcium carbonate is insoluble in water, and begins to settle to the bottom of the container in the form of a white powder. While it settles, the calcium carbonate makes the liquid look cloudy. If the liquid stands undisturbed for some time, we will find a layer of white powder (calcium carbonate) at the bottom.

Whenever a chemical reaction produces an insoluble product (see page 28), the insoluble product is called a *precipitate*. In this experiment, the calcium carbonate is a precipitate.

Carbon in Pencils and Candles

We write with lead pencils. Yet, strangely enough, the lead in a pencil is not lead at all. It is a form of carbon called graphite. In former years, the element lead was used for writing purposes, but it was found that graphite can write just as well and is much cheaper.

Ordinary candles are made of several carbon and hydrogen compounds. If we burn a candle, the carbon in it combines with oxygen from the air and forms CO_2. The hydrogen in the candle also unites with oxygen from the air to form water. (Water is a compound of hydrogen and oxygen—H_2O.) Our next experiment will show that a burning candle gives off both CO_2 and H_2O.

Melt the bottom of a small candle with a burning match, and place the candle on a table. Light the candle and cover it with a *dry* jar, as shown in Fig. 32. Wait until the candle stops burning. Examine the sides of the jar without changing its position. Do you see moisture? This is the water that was formed when the hydrogen in the candle combined with oxygen in the air.

44

Remove the jar and light the candle again. Take another jar and hold it, inverted, *above* the flame (Fig. 33) for a full minute. Then without changing the position of the jar, first extinguish the candle flame, and then cover the jar immediately with a card (Fig. 34). Turn the covered jar right side up and let its contents cool for a few minutes. Then uncover the jar, add a layer of limewater about a 1/2 - inch deep and shake. Does the limewater turn cloudy? This proves that CO_2 was formed when the carbon in the candle combined with oxygen.

The Elements in Fuels

Carbon and hydrogen are found in almost all fuels such as natural gas (used in many kitchen stoves), oil, gasoline, kerosene, soft coal and wood. All of these give off CO_2 and H_2O when they are burned.

Since paper is made from wood, we should expect to get CO_2 and H_2O when paper is burned. Repeat the last experiment, using tightly rolled paper instead of a candle and see for yourself. (*Caution!* Do this experiment in or near a sink so you can safely extinguish the paper immediately. Remove curtains and other combustible materials that may be near the sink.)

The experiments we have just performed lead us to this conclusion: *When substances containing carbon and hydrogen are burned, they combine with oxygen in the air and form CO_2 and H_2O.* This is a most interesting fact because the human breath contains CO_2 and H_2O. Would you like to prove it? Fill a test tube with a 1-inch layer of limewater. Blow your breath through a soda straw into the limewater (Fig. 35). Within a few seconds, the limewater turns cloudy, proving that you exhaled CO_2.

To prove that your breath contains water, simply place a dry, clean mirror near your mouth and blow on it. The moisture that forms on the glass (Fig. 36) shows that you exhaled water.

We Prove Food Acts as Fuel

Why do we exhale CO_2 and H_2O? The food we eat acts as

 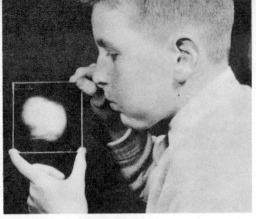

Fig. 35.　　Test your breath.　　Fig. 36.

fuel in our bodies. Like other fuels, food contains the elements carbon (C) and hydrogen (H). Inside the body, the food combines with oxygen we inhaled from the air, and slow oxidation takes place. (See page 18 for the meaning of slow oxidation.) In this process, the carbon in the food becomes carbon dioxide (CO_2) and the hydrogen in the food becomes water (H_2O). The CO_2 and H_2O are exhaled. During the slow oxidation of our food, heat energy is produced. It is this heat energy that keeps us alive.

Here is a simple experiment to show that combining food, like sugar, with oxygen from the air, will actually produce CO_2 and H_2O.

Hold a cube of sugar over a pan with tongs. Cover the sugar with a thin layer of cigarette or cigar ashes. Apply a match flame directly to the sugar, and it will start to burn (Fig. 37). Cover the burning sugar with a small jar (Fig. 38), and soon you will see moisture on the sides of the jar. This proves that water has formed. Now turn the jar right side up, and add a 1/4 - inch layer of clear limewater. Cover the jar and shake it. The limewater turns cloudy. What does this prove?

The cigarette ashes played an interesting part in this experiment. Nothing happened to the ashes but their mere presence hastened the combination of sugar with oxygen from the air. Exactly why the ashes have this effect is not known. There

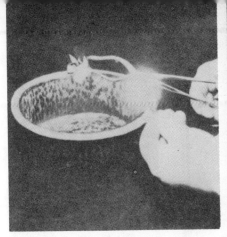

Fig. 37.   What does burning sugar produce?   Fig. 38.

are many substances whose mere presence speed up a chemical reaction, yet the substances themselves are not affected. These substances are called *catalysts*.

We Prepare Carbon Dioxide

One of man's greatest enemies is uncontrolled fire. Every year, our nation suffers a loss of many lives and millions of dollars of property because of fire. Everybody is interested in combatting this scourge of mankind, and science has made many contributions to help us fight fires. One of the important chemicals used to put out fires is our old friend carbon dioxide (CO_2). This gas has unquestionably saved many lives, homes, schools, factories, offices, and even ships from destruction. In the following experiments, we will prepare carbon dioxide and find out *why* it is useful in fire fighting.

Carbon dioxide may be obtained from vinegar and bicarbonate of soda (commonly called baking soda). Place a teaspoonful of baking soda in a small jar or glass. Add 4 teaspoons of vinegar, but do not stir. The bubbling you see (Fig. 39) is caused by the formation of carbon dioxide (CO_2). Wait until the bubbling stops. The upper portion of the jar, above the vinegar and baking soda mixture (Fig. 40), now contains carbon dioxide. To prove it, perform the following test:

47

Invisible
carbon dioxide.

Vinegar and
bicarbonate
of soda.

Fig. 39. Making   Fig. 40.   Fig. 41. Medicine
carbon dioxide.   dropper test.

Get one drop of limewater into a clean medicine dropper. Then hold the medicine dropper in the jar with the glass end above the level of the baking soda and vinegar mixture. Without letting any of the limewater drop escape from the medicine dropper, force the limewater drop to move slightly up and down inside the medicine dropper by gently squeezing and releasing the rubber bulb. Do this about 12 times. This permits the invisible carbon dioxide in the jar to mix with the limewater drop. Now examine the limewater drop. The cloudy appearance of the drop is proof that carbon dioxide was given off by the action of baking soda and vinegar (Fig. 41). This is your proof that CO_2 is present. This eye dropper method is an economical way to test for CO_2. Cover the jar or glass and save the CO_2 for the next experiment.

How was CO_2 formed in this experiment? Let's examine the equation at the top of page 49, and then study the same equation below it in terms of atoms and molecules.

The Na from the sodium bicarbonate combines with the $C_2H_3O_2$ from the acetic acid to form $NaC_2H_3O_2$. The HCO_3 of the sodium bicarbonate combines with the H of the acetic acid to form H_2CO_3 (carbonic acid). The H_2CO_3 then further breaks up into H_2O and CO_2.

$$NaHCO_3 + H(C_2H_3O_2) \longrightarrow NaC_2H_3O_2 + H_2CO_3$$

(sodium bi-   (acetic acid   yield   (sodium + (carbonic acid)
carbonate or   found in   acetate)
baking soda)   vinegar) $H_2O + CO_2$

                                                   (water)+(carbon
                                                     dioxide)

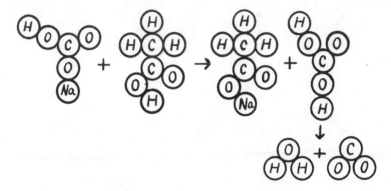

How Carbon Dioxide Puts Out Fires

Now let's find out why CO_2 is useful in fire fighting. Light a candle and place it flame downward into the jar or glass of CO_2 you have already prepared. The moment the flame is surrounded by CO_2, it is extinguished. One reason CO_2 is used in fire fighting is that it does not support combustion. That means CO_2, unlike oxygen, does not help fuels to burn. When a burning material is surrounded by CO_2, the supply of oxygen from the air is shut off, and the material stops burning.

Did you ever stop to ask: "Why doesn't the burning material combine with the oxygen in CO_2?" The reason is simple, the oxygen in CO_2 has already been combined with carbon. A burning material needs *uncombined* oxygen, like the oxygen in the air. Can you explain why a burning material does not combine with the oxygen in H_2O?

Another important reason why CO_2 is used as a fire extinguisher is that carbon dioxide is much *heavier* than air. There-

49

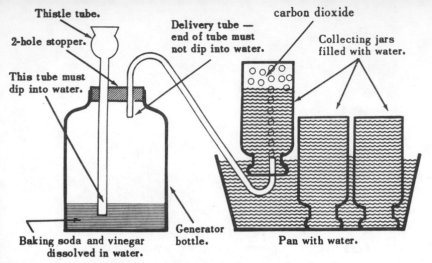

Fig. 42. Preparing and collecting carbon dioxide.

fore, it can settle on a burning object and extinguish the flames. In order to see this, we will prepare CO_2 by another method. Set up the apparatus as shown in Fig. 42.

First, remove the stopper from the generator bottle. Put 2 tablespoons of baking soda into the generator bottle. Replace the stopper and add water through the thistle tube, until the bottom of the thistle tube is covered by water. Be sure the delivery tube in the generator bottle does *not* dip into the water. Now add vinegar through the thistle tube, *a few drops at a time*, to the baking soda solution in the generator bottle. If the bubbling is too violent, it means that vinegar is being added too quickly. Collect the gas that is produced, in the same way we collected oxygen on page 20. Collect 3 or 4 jars of gas by this method.

The first jar of gas collected is a mixture of CO_2 and air. The air was forced into the jar from the generator, through the delivery tube, as CO_2 was formed. This first jar may be tested with limewater to see if any CO_2 is really present. If it is, the limewater will turn cloudy.

The second jar contains almost pure CO_2 because very little, or no air was left in the generator to reach this jar. This jar of gas will be used to prove that CO_2 is heavier than air, in the following experiment.

Pretend that the jar of CO_2 contains a liquid like water. Now, pour the invisible contents of this jar carefully into an empty glass. Test the glass for CO_2 by adding a little limewater. The limewater turns cloudy, showing that the CO_2 can be poured like a heavy fluid from one container into another. This proves that CO_2 is heavier than air.

Here is further evidence of the heaviness of CO_2: Light a candle and set it upright on a table. Keeping the third jar of CO_2 covered with a glass plate, invert it and hold it directly over the flame of the candle. Now remove the glass plate from the jar of CO_2 without changing the position of the jar. What happens to the candle? The flame is extinguished because the CO_2 "fell" out of the jar and surrounded the candle long enough to shut off the oxygen supply from the air.

Liquid and Solid CO_2

Many factories and ships have emergency containers of liquid CO_2 which are used in case of fire. Liquid CO_2 is made by compressing the gas CO_2, by means of special pumps and cooling devices. When liquid CO_2 escapes from its container, it turns into a solid material resembling snow. This has a temperature of $108°$ below zero Fahrenheit. It is very effective for extinguishing fires because it can cool the burning material as well as shut off the oxygen supply.

Solid carbon dioxide is commonly used for refrigeration purposes in trucks and in trains. The solid blocks of CO_2 are called dry ice. It is called *dry* because it leaves no liquid as it warms up, the way ordinary ice does. Dry ice changes directly from a solid into the gas CO_2 and mixes with the air. Get a small piece of dry ice from an ice cream vendor and prove that it really is CO_2 by testing it with limewater. (*Caution!* Do not touch dry ice with bare hands. The extreme cold is very injurious to the skin. Do not keep dry ice in a closed container. If the gas that forms is not permitted to escape, the container may burst with explosive force!)

We Make Foamite

Oil fires are the most difficult to put out. Water and ordinary

Fig. 43. Foamite.

chemical fire extinguishers have little effect on burning oil. A special type of fire extinguisher, foamite, has been successfully developed to combat oil fires. Foamite produces bubbles of CO_2, in a tough jelly foam, that clings and covers the burning oil. This is how you can prepare this remarkable fire fighter: Place 2 teaspoons of bicarbonate of soda in a tall drinking glass. Add 2 teaspoons of powdered gelatin and 2 teaspoons of alum. Mix the dry powders together thoroughly. Now add 6 teaspoons of vinegar and stir the mixture rapidly. Notice the heavy foam that forms. This foam contains bubbles of CO_2 that last for a long time. Hold the glass upside down, and you will see that the jelly containing the CO_2 clings firmly to the glass and does not fall out (Fig. 43). The long lasting and sticking qualities of foamite enable it to extinguish oil fires.

Many people like the tangy taste of soda water. Few know that this taste is caused by CO_2. Every kind of soda water contains large amounts of dissolved carbon dioxide gas. When you open a bottle of soda, notice bubbles of this gas escaping. It is easy to show that the gas is carbon dioxide. Pour a few teaspoons of club soda or seltzer water into a glass. Then

52

add a little limewater and stir. The resulting cloudiness proves that soda water contains carbon dioxide.

Bakers Use Carbon Dioxide

Carbon dioxide plays an important part in baking bread and cake. Bakers depend on this gas to make dough light and fluffy. This process is called *leavening*. There are two good ways of leavening dough. One is to use yeast, which consists of millions of tiny plants capable of giving off CO_2. Another method depends on the use of baking powder, which is a mixture of chemical substances that produce CO_2.

First, let's prove that a baking powder produces CO_2. Place a teaspoonful of any baking powder found in your kitchen (but *not baking soda*), into a test tube or small glass. Add a teaspoonful of water and shake gently. Notice the bubbling of gas. Now, use the medicine dropper and limewater test described on page 48. The limewater becomes cloudy when it reacts with the CO_2 that was liberated from the baking powder.

Why does CO_2 make dough light and fluffy? Let's find out. For this experiment, you will need some ordinary flour (*not a cake mix*). Place a tablespoonful of flour in a deep dish, and add 3 teaspoons of cold water. Stir the mixture thoroughly. This is dough without CO_2 (Fig. 44).

Fig. 44.   Carbon dioxide in baking.   Fig. 45.

In a second deep dish, place another tablespoonful of flour, and add one teaspoonful of baking powder. Mix these dry ingredients thoroughly. Then, add 3 teaspoons of cold water and stir the mixture well, to form dough. This dough contains CO_2. You will see the dough rise as a result of the carbon dioxide's bubbling action (Fig. 45). This kind of dough will be lighter and fluffier than the first sample you prepared. Leavened dough contains lots of small, empty spaces, and the bread made from it is easier to digest.

How does baking powder produce CO_2? To begin with, baking powder is a mixture of two substances. One is sodium bicarbonate ($NaHCO_3$). The other substance may be cream of tartar. When water is added, the $NaHCO_3$ reacts with the cream of tartar:

$$NaHCO_3 + H(KC_4H_4O_6) \longrightarrow H_2CO_3 + Na(KC_4H_4O_6)$$

| (sodium bi-carbonate) | + | (cream of tartar) | yield | (carbonic acid) | + | (Rochelle salt)· |

$$\downarrow$$

$$H_2O + CO_2$$

(water)+(carbon dioxide)

The Rochelle salt is a harmless by-product that remains in the dough. (Pure crystals of Rochelle salt are used in phonograph amplifiers.) Thus far, we have observed several ways in which carbon and carbon dioxide are used by man. However, there are thousands of other carbon compounds serving us today. The human body is composed of many varieties of carbon compounds, too. So vast is the study of carbon compounds that it has become a separate branch of chemistry called *organic chemistry*. The term *organic* refers to living things, since numerous carbon compounds are derived from living things such as plants and animals.

There are many research opportunities for the organic chemist, because of the thousands of carbon compounds that can be analyzed and synthesized.

6 - Neutralizing chemical opponents.

DID you ever try to clean tarnished or rusty metal with soap and water? It's a hopeless task. That's why special metal polish and metal cleaning agents are needed. There is nothing very mysterious about a metal cleaning agent. Here's one that you can make easily.

Place a teaspoonful of table salt in a cup, and add 4 teaspoons of vinegar. Select 2 old, dull-looking copper pennies. Wash one with soap and water. Place the other in the salt and vinegar mixture for 3 minutes (see Fig. 46), turning it over every 1/2 minute. Take the penny out of the mixture and rinse it in water. Now compare both pennies. The soap and water had practically no effect on one penny, but the vinegar and salt mixture made the other old penny appear almost new.

Many metal cleaners contain little more than the chief in-

Fig. 46. Cleaning a metal.

gredient used in our experiment. This ingredient, hydrochloric acid, was obtained from a mixture of vinegar and salt. This acid is often used to clean metals.

Acids are useful chemicals. There are many kinds of acids found in our homes. For example, vinegar contains acetic acid, lemons contain citric acid, sour milk contains lactic acid, tartaric acid is found in grapes. Rhubarb and sour apples contain malic acid. These foods have one thing in common — they all taste sour. It is the acid that gives the food its sour taste.

There is another way in which acids are alike. Let us compare the following acids:

Name of acid:	Formula:	Use:
Hydrochloric acid	HCl	It is found, naturally, in the stomach, where it aids digestion of certain foods; also used to clean metals.
Nitric acid	HNO_3	To make explosives, like TNT and nitro-glycerine.
Sulphuric acid	H_2SO_4	To clean metals, refine oil, and make other acids.
Boric acid	H_3BO_3	An eye wash.
Carbonic acid	H_2CO_3	Found in soda water. It gives soda water a slightly sour taste.

What do these formulas have in common? *They all contain hydrogen* (H). This element is found in all acids.

This does not mean that all compounds containing hydrogen are acids. Water for example is H_2O. It contains hydrogen, but it is not an acid. What is the difference between acids and other compounds that contain hydrogen? One difference is that acids taste sour but other hydrogen compounds generally do not. Another difference will be shown in the next experiment.

We Liberate Hydrogen from Acids

We are going to test the effect of the metal magnesium on an acid. Purchase magnesium ribbon (in the form of a thin, narrow strip). You will also need vinegar, a 6-inch test tube, an empty jar, and a tablespoon (see Fig. 47).

Cut the strip of magnesium into pieces, about 3/8 of an inch long, with a scissors. Pour a tablespoon of vinegar into the test tube and add a piece of magnesium ribbon. (Remember that vinegar contains acetic acid.) Notice the sizzling action as many tiny bubbles of hydrogen gas are released from the acetic acid (Fig. 48).

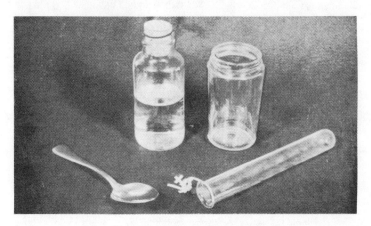

Fig. 47. Preparing to test household acids.

You can test for the hydrogen gas in the following way: Place the test tube in a jar so that the mouth of the test tube points upward. Allow the magnesium and the vinegar to react for a full minute and a half (90 seconds). Then, stand at arm's length from the test tube (Fig. 49), light a match and drop it into the test tube. You will hear a pop. This is the sound of a small explosion as the hydrogen burns and unites with oxygen from the air.

This experiment leads us to an important conclusion. *The hydrogen in an acid may be liberated by the action of certain metals, like magnesium.* This is not generally true of other compounds containing hydrogen. You may repeat the above experiments by comparing the effect of magnesium on lemon juice (which contains citric acid), and on limewater (which

57

Fig. 48. Liberating hydrogen.   Fig. 49. Testing for hydrogen.

contains Ca(OH)$_2$ and is not an acid). You will find that bubbles of hydrogen are liberated from the citric acid in lemon juice. There is no reaction when Ca(OH)$_2$ is treated with magnesium, although limewater, Ca(OH)$_2$, contains the element hydrogen.

The chemical reaction between magnesium and acetic acid (in vinegar) is shown in this equation:

$$\textbf{Mg} + 2\,\textbf{H}(\textbf{C}_2\textbf{H}_3\textbf{O}_2) \longrightarrow \textbf{H}_2 + \textbf{Mg}(\textbf{C}_2\textbf{H}_3\textbf{O}_2)_2$$

(magnesium)+(acetic acid)   yield   (hydrogen) + (magnesium acetate)

In this reaction, a molecule of magnesium reacts with 2 molecules of acetic acid, to produce one molecule of hydrogen (which contains two hydrogen atoms) and one molecule of magnesium acetate. The magnesium has replaced (taken the place of) the hydrogen in the acetic acid. In doing so, the magnesium liberated the hydrogen. As a general rule, the hydrogen in an acid can be replaced by other metals too, such as zinc, sodium and iron. Test the effect of powdered zinc on citric acid crystals or tartaric acid crystals dissolved in water.

We Test With Litmus
There is an easy way to test for the presence of an acid.

58

We use a substance called litmus. This is a natural chemical dye found in a plant known as the lichen. The litmus is extracted from this plant and blended into paper, giving us litmus paper. There are two varieties of litmus paper, red and blue. Obtain both varieties for the experiments that follow.

Fig. 50. Using litmus paper.

Place a drop of vinegar on blue litmus paper. (See Fig. 50.) The blue litmus paper turns red at once. (Remember that it's the *litmus* in the paper that is affected.) Now place a drop of ordinary water on another piece of blue litmus paper. This time the blue litmus paper remains blue. *An acid will turn blue litmus red.* To prove this, try these experiments:

Place a drop of the following liquids on blue litmus paper: lemon juice and orange juice (both contain citric acid), grape juice (contains tartaric acid), boric acid dissolved in water, citric acid crystals dissolved in water, tartaric acid crystals dissolved in water, sugar dissolved in water, and limewater. All, except the sugar dissolved in water and the limewater, turn blue litmus red.

Here are some additional substances to test with blue litmus: mayonnaise, buttermilk, apple cider, human perspiration, soda water (any flavor), pickled cucumber, grapefruit juice, pineapple juice, tomato juice and plain water. All, except water, turn blue litmus red. Can you explain the changes?

Bases
We have seen that acids turn litmus from blue to red. Some substances have the opposite effect on litmus. These substances

59

are called *bases* and they turn litmus from red to blue. Let's see this in the following experiment:

Pour a few drops of ammonia water, limewater and milk of magnesia into separate dishes; then dip a piece of blue litmus and a piece of red litmus into the contents of each dish. Notice that in each case the blue litmus did not change color, but the red litmus changed from red to blue. These three solutions contain bases. Here is a list of some common bases:

Name of base:	Formula:	Use:
Sodium hydroxide	NaOH	Commonly called lye; used in cleaning drains and in making soap.
Calcium hydroxide	Ca(OH)$_2$	Found in limewater and used by the chemist to test for CO$_2$. Also used by farmers to neutralize acid in the soil.
Ammonium hydroxide	NH$_4$OH	Commonly called ammonia water; used as a cleaning fluid.
Magnesium hydroxide	Mg(OH)$_4$	The chief ingredient in milk of magnesia; used to neutralize acid in the stomach.

If you examine the formulas of these bases, you will notice that they have one thing in common. *Bases contain the hydroxide radical, OH.* (You will recall that a radical is a group of atoms that tend to stay together.) Bases are also called alkaline substances.

Salts

We have seen that acids turn blue litmus red and bases turn red litmus blue. Now, what would happen if we used litmus to test a mixture of acid and base? Let's find out.

Place a full teaspoon of milk of magnesia into a cup. This will turn red litmus paper blue because it is a base. Then add five teaspoons of vinegar. This will turn blue litmus paper red because it contains acetic acid. Stir the mixture thoroughly with a glass rod. Then touch the wet end of the rod first to red litmus paper and then to blue litmus paper. You will find that the red litmus paper turns blue but the blue litmus paper is unaffected. This happened because you have more base in the one teaspoon of milk of magnesia than acid in the five teaspoons of vinegar. One reason for this difference is that vinegar is about 4% acetic acid and about 96% water. To have equivalent quantities of base and acid in our mixture, add more vinegar with a medicine dropper, one drop at a time. Stir thoroughly and test with litmus as before. Does the red litmus still turn blue? If it does, continue to add a single drop of vinegar, stirring and testing with red and blue litmus each time. *Keep this up until neither piece of litmus changes color.* You now have a solution which acts neither like an acid nor like a base. This is called a *neutral* solution. The acid and the base have neutralized each other as shown in this equation:

$$Mg(OH)_2 + 2H(C_2H_3O_2) \longrightarrow Mg(C_2H_3O_2)_2 + 2H_2O$$

magnesium	acetic acid	yield	magnesium acetate+ water
hydroxide +	(the acid		(a neutral com-
(the base	in vinegar)		pound, called a
in milk of			salt)
magnesia)			

In general, when a base reacts with an equivalent amount of acid, we get a neutral compound (known as a salt) and water. This rule may be written as follows:

$$\text{Base} + \text{Acid} \longrightarrow \text{A Salt} + \text{Water}$$

We can apply this rule to any acid and base, for instance:

$$NaOH + HCl \longrightarrow NaCl + H_2O$$

sodium hydroxide	hydrochloric	yield	sodium chloride	water
(base, turns red +	acid (acid		(a salt, has no +	(has no
litmus blue)	turns blue		effect on litmus)	effect on
	litmus red)			litmus)

The resulting sodium chloride (NaCl) in the above equation is ordinary table salt. This is a neutral substance. You can

61

prove sodium chloride is neutral by dissolving a teaspoonful of table salt in a glass of water and then testing the solution with red and with blue litmus. Notice that the litmus does not change color in either case.

The term "salt" does not necessarily mean table salt to the chemist. A salt is any compound (other than water) formed by neutralizing an acid with a base. Epsom salt (used as a medicine), for example, is magnesium sulfate, $MgSO_4$. It may be formed in this way:

$$Mg(OH)_2 + H_2SO_4 \longrightarrow MgSO_4 + 2H_2O$$

| magnesium hydroxide (base) | + | sulfuric acid (acid) | yield | magnesium sulfate (a salt, called Epsom salt) | + | water |

We can now understand why milk of magnesia is sometimes recommended for "stomach acidity." If there is too much acid in the stomach, we may neutralize this acid by drinking the base, magnesium hydroxide, found in milk of magnesia. One of the acids found in the human stomach is hydrochloric acid, HCl, and it reacts with milk of magnesia in this way:

$$Mg(OH)_2 + 2HCl \longrightarrow MgCl_2 + 2H_2O$$

| magnesium hydroxide (base in milk of magnesia) | + | hydrochloric acid (acid in stomach) | yield | magnesium chloride (a salt) | + | water |

The process of adding a base to an acid, to form a salt and water, is called neutralization.

We Use Indicators

A substance like litmus is very useful to the chemist since it tells him whether a material is an acid, a base or neither. We call a substance like litmus an *indicator*, because it indicates the presence of acid or base. Some fruits and vegetables contain natural chemical substances which act like indicators.

These substances may be found in tea, grape juice, and red cabbage. Here are some colorful experiments you can try with them:

(1) Prepare a cup of tea. Pour some of the tea into each of 3 test tubes, filling them 1/2 way. To the first add a teaspoonful of vinegar (acetic acid). To the second add a teaspoonful of ammonia water. Compare the 3 test tubes. The tea treated with acid has turned a pale yellow, whereas the tea treated with base (ammonia water) has turned dark brown (Fig. 51). See if you can reverse the colors by adding any base to the pale yellow solution with a teaspoon, and by adding acid to the dark brown solution.

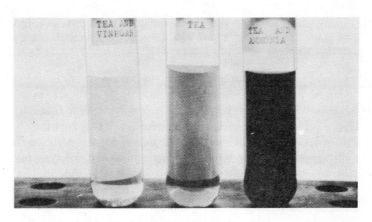

Fig. 51. Using tea as an indicator.

(2) To a quarter of a cup of grape juice, add an equal amount of water. Stir and pour some of the mixture into each of 3 test tubes, filling them 1/2 way. Proceed as before, adding a teaspoon of vinegar to one test tube, and a teaspoon of ammonia water to another. Note the change in color. Now reverse the colors by reversing the addition of acid and base.

(3) Prepare red cabbage juice by boiling some red cabbage leaves, for about 20 minutes, in a pot containing a cup of water. Use the colored juice of the cabbage, and proceed exactly as with the tea.

Colorless water solution containing phenolphthalein + ammonia = wine colored water.

Fig. 52. "Magic" with phenolphthalein.

There are several colorful artificial indicators you can test with acids and bases. These are Congo red, methyl orange and thymol blue.

We Change "Water" to "Wine"

One of the most fascinating indicators is an artificial chemical known as phenolphthalein (pronounced fee-nol-thal-een). This substance can change, in a colorless water solution, to a deep wine red in a fraction of a second by the addition of a tiny amount of any base. The deep wine red solution can then be decolorized almost instantaneously, by the addition of a little acid. Obtain a 1% solution of phenolphthalein, and use it as follows:

Add 4 or 5 drops of the phenolphthalein solution, with a medicine dropper, to 1/2 a glass, or small jar, of water and stir thoroughly. Add a few drops of ammonia water and stir. Notice the beautiful wine-red color that results (Fig. 52). Now add some vinegar and stir. The red color disappears completely. If you add more ammonia, the red color will reappear. You can keep on changing the color of the solution back and forth almost indefinitely, by using small amounts of acid and base.

Phenolphthalein is used by some magicians in "changing water into wine" or vice versa. Phenolphthalein is also used as a laxative in certain medical preparations. The chemist,

64

however, relies upon phenolphthalein as an indicator because it is so sensitive and reacts so sharply to small amounts of acid or base. This enables the chemist to detect and to measure very small quantities of acid and base with great accuracy. The use of indicators, in this way, is part of the work of the analytical chemist (a chemist who experiments with materials to learn their composition). Analytical chemistry is a fascinating field for the careful scientific worker.

7 - Finding the element
of strength - calcium.

QUEEN Cleopatra of ancient Egypt is said to have made the most extravagant drink in all history. She placed a real pearl into a glass of wine. The wine fizzed like champagne and the pearl dissolved. This was indeed an expensive drink.

What a pity that Cleopatra knew no chemistry. She could have achieved exactly the same result by using an ordinary egg shell, or a piece of marble, or some limestone, or a sea shell, or just plain chalk. Why? To the chemist, each of these materials is only a different form of calcium carbonate, $CaCO_3$. When any form of calcium carbonate is placed in wine, the result is exactly the same. How does the chemist know this? Here are some experiments which will lead us to the answer.

Since we cannot afford to experiment with pearls, let's compare a piece of chalk with an egg shell. Place a 1/2 - inch piece of chalk into a test tube and add enough vinegar to cover the chalk. Examine the chalk in the vinegar and you will see bubbles of gas forming (Fig. 53). This is carbon dioxide.

To prove that carbon dioxide has been formed, we may perform the limewater test as described on page 48.

Now examine the drop of limewater. The cloudy appearance (Fig. 54) is proof that CO_2 was given off by the action of vinegar on chalk. Why was CO_2 given off? The following equation tells the story:

$$CaCO_3 + 2\,H(C_2H_3O_2) \longrightarrow H_2CO_3 + Ca(C_2H_3O_2)_2$$

calcium carbonate (chalk) + acetic acid (vinegar) yield carbonic acid + calcium acetate

$$\downarrow$$

$$H_2O + CO_2$$

(water) + (carbon dioxide)

Fig. 53. Liberating
CO_2 from chalk.

Fig. 54. Testing for
CO_2 from chalk.

In this reaction, the CO_3 from the calcium carbonate combines with the 2H from the acetic acid, to form H_2CO_3. The H_2CO_3 then breaks up into H_2O and CO_2.

If an egg shell is nothing more than $CaCO_3$ (calcium carbonate), it should give off carbon dioxide when it is treated with vinegar. Let's find out. Crush a small piece of egg shell, about 1-inch square, into small bits and place it into a test tube. Cover with vinegar. For good results, we will need heat to increase the chemical action.

How to Heat Liquid in a Test Tube

Hold the test tube in a flame as shown in Fig. 55. Be sure to take the following precautions: (1) Use a test tube holder to grip the test tube. (2) The mouth of the test tube must never point to anyone, including yourself. If the hot liquid spatters, it will travel in the direction the test tube is pointing. (3) The test tube must be dry on the outside, otherwise it may crack when heated. (4) Keep rotating the test tube over the flame as shown in Fig. 56. This helps to avoid overheating the same spot on the test tube. (5) Use a test tube made of pyrex glass.

Continue to heat the contents of the test tube until the vinegar begins to boil; then stop and examine the test tube. Do

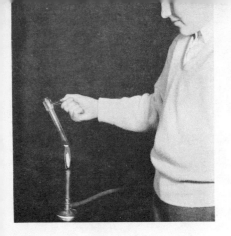

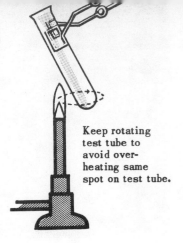

Keep rotating
test tube to
avoid over-
heating same
spot on test tube.

Fig. 55.   Heating liquid in a test tube.   Fig. 56.

you see bubbles of gas rising from the egg shell? Test this for CO_2 by using a single drop of limewater in a medicine dropper as in the last experiment. Once again you will find that the drop of limewater turns cloudy. This proves that CO_2 was formed by the action of the acid in vinegar on the calcium carbonate in the egg shell.

You can repeat the entire experiment by substituting the following in place of egg shell: a piece of sea shell, such as clam or oyster, a marble chip (not agate), and a limestone chip.

These experiments show a similarity between marble, limestone, sea shells, egg shells and chalk. Since each is a form of calcium carbonate, each gives off CO_2 when treated with acid. Now let us see the effect of heat on calcium carbonate.

We Make Quicklime

For our next experiment we need a full-length stick of chalk, a medicine dropper, red litmus paper and a pair of tongs.

Hold the stick of chalk at one end with the tongs (you may use pincers or tweezers instead). Heat the opposite end of the chalk in a *gas flame* for a full 15 minutes. The end of the chalk must be directly in the upper portion of the flame (Fig. 57). After the first minute of heating, you will notice that the underside of the chalk in the flame begins to glow brightly.

68

Fig. 57. Making quicklime.

This glowing chalk goes through a chemical change that is explained in the following equation:

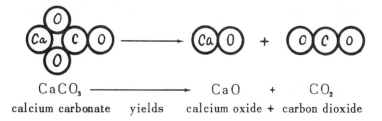

$$CaCO_3 \longrightarrow CaO + CO_2$$
calcium carbonate   yields   calcium oxide + carbon dioxide

The calcium carbonate is broken up into calcium oxide and carbon dioxide. The carbon dioxide escapes into the air. The calcium oxide remains at the end of your stick of chalk as a white material called quicklime, and glows when heated. (In former years, before the invention of the electric lamp, a bright light was produced on theater stages by heating quicklime with a gas flame. The light obtained by this method was called a limelight. Theater people still refer to the strong

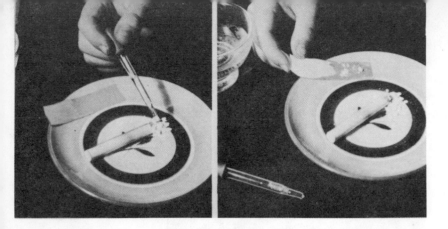

Fig. 58.   Changing quicklime to slaked lime.   Fig. 59.

light – spotlight – in the theater as the limelight, although quicklime has not been used for years.)

The heated tip of the piece of chalk has now been changed to calcium oxide (CaO) or quicklime. With the aid of a medicine dropper, place about 10 drops of water on this quicklime (Fig. 58). Notice how it puffs up and crumbles. Then, rub a piece of red litmus against the wet portion of the quicklime. Notice that the red litmus turns blue (Fig. 59). This shows us that the action of water on quicklime produced a base. All bases turn red litmus paper blue. The chemical reaction is explained in this equation:

$$CaO \quad + \quad H_2O \longrightarrow Ca(OH)_2$$

calcium oxide + water   yield   calcium hydroxide
(quicklime)   (the base)

The calcium oxide combined with the water to form the base calcium hydroxide. Calcium hydroxide, known as slaked lime, is the material from which limewater is made.

Making Limewater

To make clear limewater, place about half a teaspoonful of powdered slaked lime into a glass of cold water and stir thoroughly for a full minute. Then filter the cloudy suspension that forms with a funnel and filter paper.

70

re grade 13
Text page
382

Limestone is heated to produce carbon dioxide and calcium oxide

CALCIUM OXIDE

CO_2 CO_2 CO_2

The carbon dioxide formed is collected in tanks and sold to:

soda water manufacturers and fire extinguisher manufacturers.

Manufacturing chemist adds water to calcium oxide (or quicklime) and changes it into:

CALCIUM HYDROXIDE

Slaked lime (calcium hydroxide) is used by bricklayers. They mix it with sand and water to make mortar. Mortar holds bricks together.

Some slaked lime is dissolved in water and used as limewater.

Farmers use slaked lime as a base to neutralize acids in the soil.

Fig. 60. Limestone products.

You can make calcium oxide (CaO) and then calcium hydroxide, $Ca(OH)_2$, from each of the following materials: half an egg shell, a sea shell, a piece of limestone and a piece of marble. In each case, heat the material in a gas flame for 15 minutes, using the method shown in Fig. 57, and then add water. Test the final result with red litmus paper to find out if a base was formed.

Manufacturing chemists, making chemicals for industry, produce large quantities of calcium hydroxide in a similar way. They heat huge quantities of limestone and obtain calcium oxide and carbon dioxide. Fig. 60 illustrates how commercial

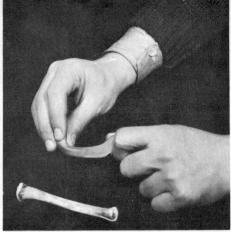

Fig. 61.   Acid softens bones.   Fig. 62.

products are produced from limestone. The following shows how the limestone molecules ($CaCO_3$) are affected:

$$CaCO_3 \longrightarrow CaO + CO_2$$

calcium carbonate   yields   calcium oxide + carbon dioxide
    (limestone)   (quicklime)

We Remove Calcium from a Bone

Calcium compounds form important parts of the human body. Our bones and our teeth are made chiefly of calcium phosphate, $Ca_3(PO_4)_2$, and calcium carbonate, $CaCO_3$. This is also true of the bones and teeth of animals and birds. How does acid affect the calcium carbonate in a chicken bone? Let's try this experiment.

You will need two similar bones taken from the legs or wings of a chicken. Scrub the bones clean with soap and steel wool to remove all the meat, fat and gristle. Place one of the bones in a test tube or jar and cover it with vinegar (Fig. 61). Allow the bone to soak for 10 days, changing the vinegar every third day. As the acid in the vinegar reacts with the calcium carbonate in the bone, the calcium carbonate grad-

72

ually dissolves. At the end of 10 days the bone will become so soft that you may be able to bend it without breaking it. Compare this with the other bone that has not been treated with acid (Fig. 62).

Since teeth also contain calcium carbonate, you can see why it is important to avoid an acid condition of the mouth. Particles of food which remain in your mouth may decay and form acids. These acids slowly dissolve the calcium carbonate in the teeth and eventually form cavities. That's why cleaning your teeth regularly is so important. You can test the fluid in your mouth, to see if it contains acid, with a piece of blue litmus.

Tooth pastes and tooth powders sometimes contain bases which neutralize the acids in the mouth. To see if your tooth-paste contains a base, mix some of it with water and test it with a piece of red litmus paper. If it turns blue, you know that the toothpaste contains a base.

We Make a Plaster Mold

Have you ever known someone who had a broken arm or leg? When such an injury occurs, the doctor usually places the broken limb in a plaster cast. This cast is made from a powdered variety of calcium sulfate called plaster of Paris. The plaster of Paris is mixed with water to form a soft paste which can be molded into any shape. Within a few minutes after water is added to the powder, the paste hardens automatically into a solid material. That is why it is used to set broken bones quickly. Plaster of Paris is also used to make an exact impression of an object. In our next experiment, we will make a plaster cast of a key.

You will need plaster of Paris, a little oil (salad oil or light lubricating oil), a key, a cup and an old tablespoon. Select a key with raised lettering on it.

Place a heaping tablespoon of plaster of Paris in the cup and mix it with enough water to make a thick, creamy, wet paste. Use the spoon to transfer all the paste to a large sheet of paper. Build up a small mound of the paste. Now cover the entire key with a thin coating of oil by rubbing it on with

Fig. 63.   Making a plaster mold.   Fig. 64.

your fingers. Then press the key *flat into* the mound of paste, leaving the top side of the key uncovered (Fig. 63).

Wait 15 minutes while the plaster hardens completely. Remove the key carefully and examine the plaster. Notice that it has become a hard mass and that it now has an impression of the key, including the letters (Fig. 64).

From Plaster to Gypsum

Why does powdered plaster of Paris harden so quickly when water is added? Because it is composed of a form of calcium sulfate that has the power to combine chemically with water. The result of this chemical combination is a hard substance called gypsum. The formula for gypsum is $CaSO_4.2H_2O$. This formula tells us that each molecule of $CaSO_4$ (calcium sulfate) has combined with two molecules of water. The chemical combination between the calcium sulfate and water takes place rather quickly. Therefore, the plaster sets, or hardens, quickly.

Calcium may be called the element of hardness. Nature uses calcium carbonate as a hard protective coat for oysters, clams, snails and birds' eggs. Another hard, protective coat is the pearl that develops inside an oyster's body to safeguard it against certain irritating substances. Man depends on the hardness of limestone and marble when he builds houses, mansions and palaces from these forms of calcium carbonate. The calcium compound in mortar that holds our brick buildings together must be hard, too. Even our very bones and teeth depend on calcium for their hardness. That is why calcium may be called the element of hardness.

74

8 - Making man modern with metals.

THIS is a remarkable age. Rockets and satellites flash through space at fantastic speeds. Jet planes streak across the sky flying 800 miles an hour. It's a commonplace experience to travel in a 300 horsepower automobile at a mere 60 miles per hour. We pass through skyscraper cities, under rivers through tunnels, and over rivers across immense bridge spans. The telephone, radio and television keep us in touch with all parts of the globe. We truly live in a world of machines.

Satellites, rockets, jet planes, automobiles, skyscrapers, tunnels, mile-long bridges, telephones, television sets and machines! These are the products of modern times; but did you know that they all began in the laboratory? They are the result of scientific teamwork involving metallurgy, the chemistry of metals.

Think what kind of world this would be if we did not know how to extract metals from the earth and if we did not know the chemical properties of metals! In this chapter we will find out why metals are so important in the making of modern machines and structures. We will discover some of the interesting ways in which metals react.

First, collect the following metals: A piece of aluminum wrapping foil, a piece of copper wire, a nickel, a silver coin, an iron nail, an old razor blade and a tin can.

The most noticeable property of the metals we have assembled is their shiny appearance, or *metallic lustre*. All of the chemical elements known to science have been divided into two main groups: the metals which have a lustre, and the non-metals which do not. Sulfur, carbon, and oxygen are examples of non-metals.

Test the metals with a magnet. You will find that only the iron and steel (which contains iron) are attracted by a magnet. The tin can is attracted, too, because the can contains iron

75

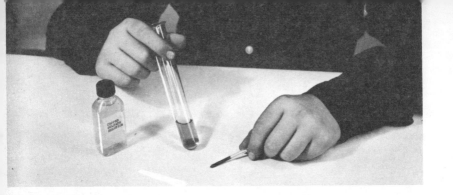

Fig. 65. Coating a nail with copper.

below the layer of tin. Pure tin is not attracted by a magnet. Try testing a Canadian nickel with a magnet. This coin has a higher percentage of nickel than the U.S. coin. Pure, or almost pure nickel is attracted by a magnet.

We Extract Copper

There are many compounds which contain metals. The chemist has discovered clever ways of getting the pure metal from a compound. In the next experiment we will obtain pure copper from the compound copper sulfate. You will need an iron nail (about 2 inches long), a 6-inch test tube, a teaspoon, and some copper sulfate.

Dissolve 1/4 teaspoon of copper sulfate in 1/4 test tube of warm water. Clean the nail to a shiny brightness by using steel wool and rubbing it with a mixture of vinegar and salt. Rinse the nail and place it into the blue copper sulfate solution. At the end of 5 minutes, remove the nail and examine it (Fig. 65). What has happened? As if by magic, the nail appears to have changed into red copper. Actually there is only a thin coating of copper on the nail. How did this happen? The following reaction took place between the iron nail and the copper sulfate:

$$Fe \;+\; CuSO_4 \longrightarrow Cu \;+\; FeSO_4$$

iron + copper sulfate   yield   copper + iron sulfate
(the nail)   (in the solution)   (which enters
                                    the solution).

76

Fig. 66. Extracting mercury.

Some of the iron in the nail replaced the copper in the copper sulphate to form a new compound, *iron sulfate*. The replaced copper comes out of the solution as uncombined copper, and forms a thin coating around the nail. The new compound, iron sulfate, being soluble, enters the solution.

Mercury from Mercurochrome

You can make a penny look like silver by extracting mercury from a mercury compound and then coating the penny with it. For this experiment you will need mercurochrome. This is a mercury compound. In addition, you will need a sparkling clean penny (brightened by rubbing salt and vinegar on it with steel wool), a piece of aluminum foil about 3 inches square, bicarbonate of soda, and an old pie plate (which is *not* to be used for food afterwards).

Place the sparkling clean penny in the center of the aluminum foil. Fold the sides of the foil upward to make a small cup with the penny inside the cup.

Now place the aluminum foil cup (with the penny in it)

into the pie plate and set it on a gas stove, but do not light the gas yet. To the penny add 10 drops of mercurochrome, 1/2 teaspoonful of water, and 1/2 teaspoonful of bicarbonate of soda (Fig. 66). Then light the gas and heat the pie plate with a very small flame. As soon as the liquid boils away, add another 1/2 teaspoon of water to the penny. Keep on boiling away the liquid and adding 1/2 teaspoons of water for a full 10 minutes; then turn off the gas. Allow the materials to cool for another 10 minutes, and place the pie plate into a sink free of other dishes and silverware. *(Caution!* Mercury compounds are injurious when taken internally. Although we have used very small amounts of mercurochrome, let's take no chances! *Do not let any of the materials used in this experiment come in contact with dishes or silverware to be used for meals.* If you suspect a dish of having been contaminated with a mercury compound, wash it thoroughly with plenty of soap and warm water.) Without touching the materials, flush the pie plate and its contents for 5 minutes with warm water from a faucet. When everything has been flushed clean, examine the penny. It seems to have turned into silver, but it is merely coated with a thin layer of mercury. Take a paper towel or a cloth and rub the penny for a few minutes in order to make the silvery color more noticeable. Examine the penny again after a few days and see what has happened. Remember that all is not silver that glitters like silver. (After you have finished this experiment, discard the used aluminum foil. Do not use the pie plate for food.)

In this experiment, the element copper in the penny, and the element aluminum in the aluminum foil, reacted with the mercury compound, mercurochrome. This reaction liberated the element mercury. Both the aluminum foil and the penny received a coating of mercury, but the mercury was more noticeable on the copper penny than on the silvery aluminum.

We Electroplate

Did you ever see a gold plated ring? It looks like solid gold. In reality, it is made of a cheap material (like brass) and has a thin layer of gold coating it. It is quite easy to coat a cheap material with a shiny metal like gold, silver or copper. The process most commonly used to do this is called electro-plating. In our next experiment we will do electro-plating by coating a carbon rod with a layer of copper.

Assemble the materials shown in Fig. 67, and note the following instructions:

(1) The carbon rods may be found inside old dry cells used in flashlights.

(2) The solution is prepared by dissolving 1/4 teaspoon of gelatin and 2 teaspoons of copper sulphate in a glass of warm water.

(3) Do not allow the carbon rods to come in contact with each other.

(4) Make all connections as shown in Fig. 67, and allow the current to run for 5 minutes. Then disconnect any one of the wires attached to either dry cell.

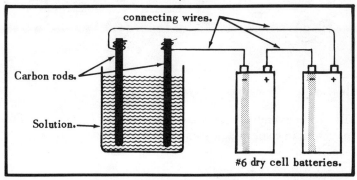

Fig. 67. Electroplating.

Now remove both carbon rods from the solution. The carbon rod attached to the plus pole was not affected, but the carbon rod attached to the minus pole is covered with a layer of shiny copper. The electric current has liberated the element copper from the copper sulfate.

Try nickel plating a carbon rod by the same method, but use a solution of 2 teaspoons of nickel ammonium sulfate, half teaspoon of boric acid and half teaspoon of ammonium chloride dissolved in a glass of warm water.

79

These experiments illustrate the way the chemist makes copper plated ash trays, nickel plated towel racks, gold plated watches, silver plated spoons and chromium plated automobile bumpers. The chief difference between any two of these is the solution used. In copper plating, the solution must contain a compound of copper; in gold plating the solution must contain a compound of gold.

We Extract Metal from Ore

Most metals are found in the earth as compounds. The metal lead, for instance, is found in the earth not as uncombined lead but as the compound lead oxide. How can we get pure lead from this compound? The chemist uses the element carbon to remove the oxygen from the lead oxide as follows:

$$2\ PbO\ +\ C\ \longrightarrow\ 2\ Pb\ +\ CO_2$$

lead oxide   +   carbon   yield   lead   +   carbon dioxide

The carbon unites with the oxygen in the lead oxide. This produces uncombined lead and carbon dioxide. In our next experiment we will prepare lead from yellow lead oxide.

You will need 1/2 teaspoon of lead oxide. Mix this with one and a half teaspoons of powdered charcoal. Place the mixture in a *pyrex* test tube. Then arrange the apparatus as shown in Fig. 68. We must use a Bunsen burner to obtain a high temperature. The limewater is used to show that carbon dioxide is also formed in the reaction. After the apparatus has been arranged, proceed as follows:

Light the burner and open the air holes until you obtain a blue flame. At the beginning, avoid overheating the test tube by moving the flame slowly back and forth *under the mixture in the test tube*. After heating in this way for a full minute, hold the burner *in one position* under the mixture, until the mixture begins to glow. To do this successfully, the under surface of the test tube must be in the hottest part of the flame as shown in Fig. 68. Move the flame to a new position under the mixture every 2 minutes and keep the mixture glowing for a full 15 minutes. (It is important to keep the underside of the test tube in the hottest part of the flame throughout this heating process.)

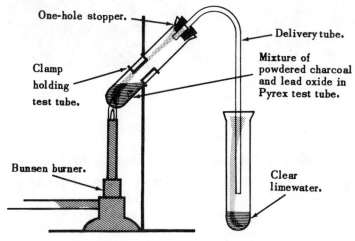

Fig. 68. Extracting pure lead.

When you have finished heating, examine the limewater and you will find that it has turned cloudy. Evidently, carbon dioxide was produced when the carbon united with the oxygen in the lead oxide.

Be sure that the test tube has cooled off. Wait about 10 minutes. Then pour the contents of the test tube into a jar of cold water. Place the jar under a water faucet and let cold water run rapidly into the jar. The carbon is a light material and it floats off. When all the carbon has been removed, examine the bottom of the jar and you will find tiny balls of shiny lead. Take one of the balls of lead and see if you can write with it on paper.

You may liberate copper from black copper oxide by mixing

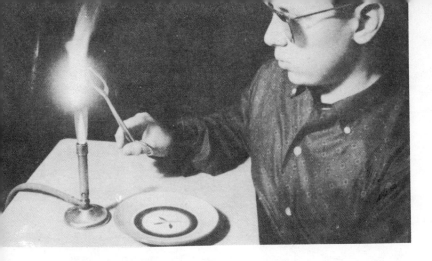

Fig. 69. Magnesium unites with oxygen.

half a teaspoon of copper oxide with one and a half teaspoons of powdered charcoal, and heating as in the last experiment.

The method of obtaining lead from lead oxide, or copper from copper oxide, by heating with carbon, is also used to obtain tin from tin oxide, or zinc from zinc oxide, or iron from iron oxide. For example, in the United States alone, over 30 million tons of iron are made by this method every year:

$$2 Fe_2O_3 + 3C \longrightarrow 4 Fe + 3 CO_2$$

iron oxide + carbon   yield   iron + carbon dioxide

Magnesium is Different

Most metals unite with oygen, but the metal magnesium does this in a very spectacular way. In our next experiment we will study the reaction between magnesium and the oxygen in the air. We need a pair of tongs, a 1-inch strip of magnesium ribbon, a saucer, a stirring rod, and a piece of red litmus paper. In addition, it is advisable to wear sun glasses. (*Caution!* Do not look directly into the flame that will be produced in this reaction unless you wear sun glasses. This experiment is quite safe if you use the recommended amount of

Fig. 70. Collecting
magnesium oxide.

Fig. 71. Magnesium
burns in carbon dioxide.

magnesium ribbon, and if you handle it with tongs as directed.)

Hold the 1-inch strip of magnesium with the tongs and ignite it in a gas flame or in a Bunsen burner (Fig. 69). As soon as the magnesium begins to burn, hold it over the saucer to catch the ashes that form (Fig. 70). Notice the extremely brilliant white flame that is produced. (Magnesium is used in signal flares for aviators and sailors lost at sea. The bright light of burning magnesium can be seen for many miles.)

Now examine the ashes that have dropped into the saucer. This white substance is magnesium oxide. It was formed as follows:

$$2 \text{ Mg} + \text{O}_2 \longrightarrow 2 \text{ MgO}$$

magnesium + oxygen   yield   magnesium oxide
(in the air)

Add 3 or 4 drops of water to the white ashes (magnesium oxide) with a medicine dropper, and then stir with the glass rod. Dip the corner of a piece of red litmus into the solution.

The red litmus turns blue because a base has been formed. Which base? The following equation will explain:

$$MgO \quad + \quad H_2O \longrightarrow Mg(OH)_2$$

magnesium oxide + water   yield   magnesium hydroxide
(white ashes)   (a base)

The base is magnesium hydroxide. In Chapter VI, we learned that magnesium hydroxide is found in milk of magnesia. Think of it! Magnesium metal is used in making flares, but its ashes can be used to make a laxative.

The brilliant flame produced when magnesium burns illustrates the great chemical attraction between magnesium and oxygen. You will remember that carbon dioxide is used to extinguish fires. Let's find out if it can extinguish the flame of burning magnesium. To see this unusual occurrence, first prepare a jar of carbon dioxide as follows: Place a teaspoonful of bicarbonate of soda into a small jar and add 4 teaspoons of vinegar, but do not stir the mixture. When the bubbling ceases, light a match and place the flame inside the jar. Notice that the flame is extinguished as soon as it enters the jar. This proves that the jar contains enough carbon dioxide to extinguish ordinary fires.

Put on your sun glasses and grasp a 2-inch strip of magnesium ribbon with the tongs. Ignite the magnesium in a gas flame and, without dropping the burning magnesium, hold it in the jar of CO_2 (see Fig. 71). The magnesium continues to burn.

Why does magnesium burn when it is surrounded by CO_2? In order for a substance to burn, it must have a supply of oxygen. Magnesium has a great attraction for oxygen, and it can take oxygen away from carbon dioxide and continue burning. Other substances cannot do this. The following reaction takes place between magnesium and carbon dioxide:

$$2\ Mg\ +\ CO_2 \longrightarrow 2\ MgO\ +\ C$$

magnesium + carbon dioxide   yield   magnesium oxide + carbon

If you examine the white magnesium oxide produced, you will see several black spots on it. These are particles of carbon.

Earlier in this chapter we learned that all elements are divided into two classes: metals and non-metals. We have just observed magnesium, a metal, combining with oxygen, a non-metal. Chemical elements obey a rule of opposites when they unite to form compounds. In general, *metals combine with non-metals*.

We Change a Negative into a Photo

As another illustration of this rule, we will transform a black photograph negative into a "white picture." All we need is an old negative, some tincture of iodine, a pair of tongs and a saucer. First, notice that the negative has a black material on it. This is silver in the form of a very fine powder. Now place the negative in the saucer (Fig. 72), and cover it completely with tincture of iodine. Let the iodine remain in contact with the negative for about 15 minutes, turning the negative over every minute with the tongs, in order to wet all of the surface. Then wash the saucer and its contents free of iodine by letting cold water from a faucet run over it. Examine the negative. The black silver has changed to a yellowish white. You may remove the excess iodine by dipping the negative into a dish of ammonia water. The negative now looks like a positive or a print (Fig. 73). Place it over a dark background, and you will see the black and white picture as it appears in a print.

Fig. 72.   Negative changed to photo.   Fig. 73.

What caused this change to take place? The iodine, a non-metal, combined with the silver, a metal, as follows:

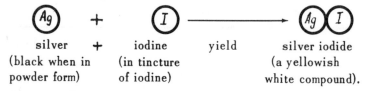

silver   +   iodine   yield   silver iodide
(black when in   (in tincture   (a yellowish
powder form)   of iodine)   white compound).

We Temper Steel

Steel is one of the wonder metals of the world. The same piece of steel can be changed from hard to soft, from soft to springy, from springy to hard and vice versa. To see how this can be done, we need a gas burner, a candle, a pair of tongs, a jar of cold water and 3 old double-edge razor blades. (Here's a chance to get rid of those used razor blades that accumulate in the medicine chest.)

Remember that the blades won't cut you if you avoid touching the sharp edges. Note how springy these steel blades are by bending one. When you let go with one hand, the blade springs back into shape. The ability of a material to regain its shape is called elasticity. The razor blade is made of an elastic metal.

Now grasp the extreme end of one blade with a pair of

Fig. 74.   Steel loses its springiness.   Fig. 75.

tongs, and heat the blade in a gas flame (Fig. 74). Wait until
the entire blade is red hot. Then remove the blade from the
flame, and continue holding it with the tongs for about 5 minutes until it cools off. Take the blade by both ends and bend
it as before. What happens? The steel has become so soft that it
no longer springs back into shape but it remains bent. See
Fig. 75.

Heat the second blade as before. Wait until the entire blade
is red hot. Then, *before it loses its redness,* act quickly and
plunge the blade into the jar of cold water. It will sizzle as
it cools off. Take the blade out of the water and try to bend
it as before. What happens this time? The steel has become
so hard and brittle that it snaps in two. See Fig. 75. One
method of making steel hard consists of heating it to a certain
temperature and then plunging the hot steel into a special
cooling bath. By controlling the temperature of the cooling
bath, the steel is made hard without becoming too brittle.

Can the springiness or elasticity of steel be restored? Try the
following and see for yourself.

Heat the third razor blade to redness. Plunge it into the jar

87

of cold water as before. We know that this treatment made the steel hard and brittle. Now we will try to restore its springiness.

Light the candle. Grasp the blade at the extreme end with your tongs. Now heat the blade in the candle flame for exactly 15 seconds and plunge it immediately into cold water. Test the blade for springiness as before. Notice that the blade has regained most of its elasticity.

The properties of steel depend upon the temperature to which it is heated and the temperature at which it is cooled. Controlling the elasticity of steel by heating and cooling is known as *tempering*.

Because its properties can be varied, steel is one of the most valuable metals in the world. Recently, American scientists produced an amazingly tough steel. A cable two inches in diameter, made of this steel, can withstand a force of one million pounds. Imagine the strength such steel will impart to machines, buildings, and bridges that are made of it. There are wonderful opportunities for research and discovery in the fascinating field of metallurgy, the chemistry of metals, so important to the construction of machines, bridges, tunnels, missiles, and rockets to the moon. The world is waiting for scientists to produce supermetals which can cope with the tremendous forces and extreme temperatures to be encountered in man's conquest of outer space.

9 - Testing food for thought.

FAMINE is one of man's greatest problems. That is why scientists are constantly seeking new ways to provide us with more food. In 1902 the Nobel Prize for the world's most outstanding discovery in chemistry was awarded to a German scientist named Emil Fischer. What did he discover? A way of making sugar artificially from its elements carbon, hydrogen and oxygen! Hitherto, every food had come from plants and animals. Now, for the first time in history, a mere mortal made a food artificially. Emil Fischer proved that it was possible to make a real food from chemical substances. This, indeed, was a great step forward in man's battle against hunger.

We believe that the day must come when chemists will discover how to make food, good food, in large quantities without relying on plants and animals. Before we have completed this chapter, we will see how foods can be made artificially. In performing the experiments which lie ahead, we will become acquainted with a subject that is vital to all of us, *the chemistry of food.*

What is Food?

What does the scientist regard as food? This may seem like a foolish question to those of us who think anything is food if it is fit to eat. Yet, goats eat newspaper. Does this mean the animal doesn't know any better, or is paper a food for goats? No matter what goats may think, paper is not a food because it fails to give nourishment. To qualify as a food, a substance must be able to nourish a living thing in at least one of three ways: provide energy, provide material for growth and repair of the body, and keep the body in good health. Paper can do none of these things for goats or for humans, but milk, an excellent food, can do all of these things. Why?

89

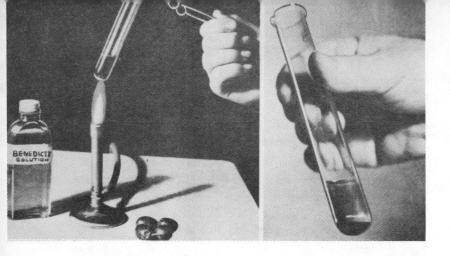

Fig. 76.   Testing for sugar.   Fig. 77.

Milk contains certain natural chemical compounds called nutrients which can nourish the body, but paper does not contain a single nutrient. Every real food contains at least one nutrient.

One of our favorite nutrients is sugar. There are many different kinds of sugar. Two of the most commonly used sugars are sucrose, whose formula is $C_{12}H_{22}O_{11}$, and glucose, whose formula is $C_6H_{12}O_6$. Sucrose is extracted from sugar cane and beets, and is used in our homes as granulated sugar and sugar tablets. Glucose is found in most sweet fruits.

We Test for Glucose

A molecule of glucose, $C_6H_{12}O_6$, is smaller than a molecule of sucrose, $C_{12}H_{22}O_{11}$. Therefore, glucose is regarded as a simple sugar. Our first experiment will be a chemical test for this simple sugar. (See Fig. 76 for the materials needed.)

Obtain some Benedict's solution in a drug store or chemical supply house. Fill about 3/4 of an inch of a test tube with this blue solution. Using a test tube holder, heat the liquid gently over a flame. *Caution!* Read the directions on page 67 for heating liquids in a test tube (Figs. 55 and 56). Allow it to boil for 10 seconds and stop. The Benedict's solution has not as yet changed color. Now add 1/2 of a raisin or 1/2 of a grape to the solution and reheat to boiling. Let it boil for about 10 seconds. What happens this time? The blue solution may go through a whole series of color changes but it finally becomes a red-brown or yellow-brown. Allow the test tube to stand for 5 minutes and you will find that a brown, powdery substance (a precipitate) has settled to the bottom (Fig. 77). The formation of a brown color or a brown precipitate, when a substance is heated with Benedict's solution, is a test for a *simple sugar*. We use this same method to test other fruits for the presence of a simple sugar. Try the Benedict test on small pieces (or on about 10 drops of the juice) of the following fruits: apple, orange, pineapple, peach, plum, pear, grapefruit, banana, apricot and lemon. In each test, the blue Benedict's solution turns brown, showing that all of these fruits contain simple sugar.

Does it surprise you to learn that a sour lemon contains sugar? This is exactly what our experiment has proven. We don't normally think of a lemon as containing sugar because this fruit also contains citric acid. The sour taste of the acid disguises the presence of sugar. This shows that you can be fooled if you depend on your sense of taste to tell if sugar is present, but chemicals like Benedict's solution cannot be fooled.

We see, then, that some foods may contain sugar although they do not taste sweet. On the other hand, some foods do *not* contain sugar although they *do* taste sweet. How is this possible? There are several artificial chemical substances, like saccharine and sucaryl, which taste very sweet but they are not sugar. These are not nutrients, since they do not nourish the body. (That's what makes them popular with people trying to reduce.) In our next experiment, we will test some saccharine or sucaryl with Benedict's solution.

Dissolve a saccharine tablet or a sucaryl tablet in 1/4 of a glass of water and taste it. It is quite sweet. Test 10 drops of this sweet liquid with Benedict's solution as described on page 90. No matter how long you boil the liquid, it remains blue, proving that sucaryl and saccharine contain no sugar.

While we can't taste the difference between candy

containing glucose $(C_6H_{12}O_6)$ and candy containing sucrose $(C_{12}H_{22}O_{11})$, Benedict's solution reacts quite differently to each of these sugars. Test the effect of sucrose on Benedict's solution by using 1/4 of a teaspoon of granulated sugar, and following the same method as before. This time the solution remains blue because the granulated sugar is not a simple sugar.

Now perform the last test in a different way. Dissolve 1/4 of a teaspoon of granulated sugar in 1/4 of a test tube of water. Add 3 drops of Benedict's solution with a medicine dropper. Heat the mixture to boiling. *Caution!* To prevent being spattered by hot liquid, point the test tube *away* from all persons and keep moving the test tube in and out of the flame continually. Continue to boil the liquid for 5 minutes, and the blue solution will turn brown.

How do we explain this? When sucrose is boiled in water, the sucrose gradually reacts with the water to form simple sugar. The following equation tells the story:

$$C_{12}H_{22}O_{11} + H_2O \longrightarrow C_{12}H_{24}O_{12} \longrightarrow \begin{matrix} C_6H_{12}O_6 \\ + \\ C_6H_{12}O_6 \end{matrix}$$

1 molecule of sucrose + 1 molecule of water	1 large theoretical molecule of sucrose and water combined.	2 molecules of simple sugar formed by splitting of theoretical large molecule.

Changing sucrose into a simple sugar, like glucose, requires the presence of a catalyst. In this experiment, one of the substances in Benedict's solution acted as the catalyst.

We Test for Starch

Sugar is an important nutrient; it supplies us with energy. When we eat more sugar than the body needs, the excess turns into fat. Another nutrient that behaves exactly like sugar is starch. If you are overweight, your doctor may advise you to avoid eating too many starchy foods. He may even give you a list of foods to avoid because they are rich in starch. Such a list is made possible by the work of the chemist who knows how to test foods for starch. Here is a chemical test for starch:

Place 1/4 of a teaspoon of cornstarch or laundry starch in a test tube. Fill the test tube 1/4 with water and then add 3 or 4 drops of tincture of iodine. Shake the mixture. Notice the dark blue-black color that is formed. Save this for the next experiment. The formation of a blue-black color, when iodine is added, shows the presence of starch. Repeat the iodine test, using sugar instead of starch, and you will find that no blue-black color is produced.

Chemists do not know whether iodine and starch really combine chemically to form a blue-black product. The mystery surrounding the reaction between iodine and starch is shown by the following experiment:

Place the test tube containing the blue-black product you made, in a test tube holder. Heat over a flame until it begins to boil. The blue color disappears completely! Now place the lower part of the test tube under cold water from a faucet. Before a full minute has passed, the blue color will reappear.

Scientists may disagree about the actual chemical combination of iodine and starch, but they do agree that iodine is a reliable test for starch. Therefore, let's use iodine to find out which foods contain starch. Place a small amount of food (about the size of a pea) in a test tube. If the food is dry, add about 3 or 4 drops of water to moisten it. Then add 3 or 4 drops of iodine to the food. Try this with the following foods: potato, bread, any cereal, cake, spaghetti or noodles, milk, dry cocoa, cheese, fish and butter. All except milk, cheese, fish and butter turn blue-black. Can you explain why?

Starch is often added to certain kinds of paper to improve their quality. Writing paper usually contains starch to prevent the ink from becoming blurred. Newspaper does not contain starch (if it did, goats might derive some nourishment from it). Place a drop of tincture of iodine on each of the following

93

and note what happens: newspaper, facial tissue, a paper bag, a sheet of writing paper and a paper towel.

We Change Starch to Sugar

Every time we eat starchy foods, the starch changes into sugar. Let's see this for ourselves. First, test 1/4 teaspoon of starch with blue Benedict's solution as described on page 90. The blue Benedict's solution remains unchanged, showing that no simple sugar is present. Now place 1/4 teaspoon of starch in another test tube. Add a teaspoon of warm (not hot) water. Then place some saliva into the test tube and shake it gently to mix with the starch and water. Keep the contents warm by putting the test tube into a glass of warm water for 5 minutes. Then test this mixture for sugar by adding 4 or 5 drops of Benedict's solution with a medicine dropper. Dry the outside of the test tube and heat its contents to boiling. This time, the solution turns from blue to brown. This proves that some of the starch has been changed into sugar.

How does saliva change starch into sugar? The formula for starch is $C_6H_{10}O_5$. Under certain conditions starch reacts chemically with water as follows:

$$C_6H_{10}O_5 \quad + \quad H_2O \longrightarrow C_6H_{12}O_6$$

starch $\quad+\quad$ water $\qquad$ yield $\qquad\qquad$ glucose
(simple sugar)

To understand what has happened, simply add the atoms in starch to the atoms in water, like this:

$$
\begin{array}{ll}
C_6H_{10}O_5 & (\text{starch}) \\
+ \quad H_2O & (\text{water}) \\
\hline
C_6H_{12}O_6 & (\text{simple sugar})
\end{array}
$$

total

Just what has saliva to do with changing starch into sugar? The reaction requires a catalyst. Human saliva has a natural catalyst called *ptyalin* which causes starch to react with water and produce sugar.

94

The chemist has learned how to imitate nature. He has discovered how to change starch into sugar by using an artificial catalyst, hydrochloric acid. By this method, more than half a million pounds of cornstarch are converted into sugar each year in the United States alone. This process is used in making many sweet syrups like Karo, as well as sugar for candy.

Changing Sawdust to Sugar

One of the truly remarkable achievements of chemistry is the changing of sawdust into real sugar. This scientific miracle is not difficult to understand when we know that the chief compound in sawdust is cellulose with the formula $C_6H_{10}O_5$. Cellulose is very much like starch, which has the same formula $C_6H_{10}O_5$, but the two are not the same. There are several reasons for this[*]. For one, their atoms are arranged differently. This is very much like comparing the words *knee* and *keen*. Each word consists of one k, one n, and two e's, but they are not the same because their letters are arranged somewhat differently. Nevertheless, cellulose, like starch, can be made to react with water and this is what happens:

$$C_6H_{10}O_5 \ + \ H_2O \longrightarrow C_6H_{12}O_6$$

cellulose + water   yield   simple sugar
(glucose)

This reaction also requires the use of an acid as a catalyst. The final product is the simple sugar, glucose.

The changing of sawdust into sugar illustrates how the chemist can change waste material into a real food. No one would think of putting sawdust into a cup of tea, but it is quite safe and nourishing to use the sugar made from sawdust.

We Test for Fats

Many of our foods contain the energy giving nutrient called fat. This is, of course, the compound that makes certain meats greasy. There are several different kinds of fat, each with a

[*]You may wish to consult a text for the meaning of $(C_6H_{10}O_5)_x$.

complicated formula. Here are some of the common fats we find in our food:

Name of fats:	Formula:	Where it is found:
Stearin or glyceryl-tri-stearate	$C_3H_5(C_{18}H_{35}O_2)_3$	In meats.
Olein or glyceryl-tri-oleate	$C_3H_5(C_{18}H_{33}O_2)_3$	In meats and vegetable oils.
Butyrin or glyceryl-tri-butyrate	$C_3H_5(C_4H_7O_2)_3$	In butter and milk.

In spite of the complicated formulas, you will notice that each of the fats contains the glyceryl radical, C_3H_5. This part of the fat can be changed into the valuable chemical glycerine, $C_3H_5(OH)_3$, used in making the high explosive, nitroglycerine. When your butcher trims the fat off lamb chops and steaks, he does not throw the fat away. He sells it to a chemical concern that manufactures glycerine.

Here is an easy way to test for fat. Place a drop of salad oil (which is almost pure fat) on a piece of paper and rub it into the paper gently, with your finger. Place a drop of water on another piece of paper and rub it in gently, too. Keep both pieces of paper in a warm place (in the sunlight or near a radiator) for about 5 minutes. Then hold both papers against a strong light and examine them. The drop of water dried up and no light comes through. The oil has left a spot that is still moist. This is called a translucent spot because it allows light to come through. All fats produce a translucent spot on paper which does not disappear when warmed for a few minutes. Rub a small amount of the following food into paper and see if you obtain such a spot: butter, Swiss cheese, cottage cheese, mayonnaise or salad dressing, cream, peanut or any other nut, bacon, lettuce, carrot, lard or crisco.

The cottage cheese, lettuce and carrot do not produce a translucent spot. The others do. If you want to avoid eating fatty foods, you can identify them by this test, but don't begin experimenting when there's company for dinner.

Fig. 78. Extracting pure fat.

We Extract Pure Fat from Chocolate

In our next experiment we will extract the pure fat from chocolate. You will need a non-flammable solvent, like carbona or carbon-tetrachloride. If you are not sure whether the fluid is non-flammable, read the label carefully. You will also need a piece of chocolate about 1-inch square and 1/4 - inch thick, two 6-inch test tubes, a cork to fit the test tubes, a funnel and filter paper, a teaspoon, a saucer and a cup.

Mash the chocolate in the cup with the spoon. Transfer the mashed chocolate to one of the test tubes. Add enough cleaning fluid to fill 3/4 of the test tube. Insert the cork and shake the test tube vigorously for a full minute.

Prepare a filter paper and put it in the funnel, but do not moisten the filter paper with water. Insert the stem of the funnel into the other test tube. Pour the chocolate and cleaning fluid mixture through the filter (Fig. 78). Place the saucer on a window sill and open the window wide. Then pour the

Fig. 79. Pouring
dissolved fat.

Fig. 80. Pure
fat in saucer.

fluid that came through the filter into the saucer (Fig. 79). *Avoid inhaling the fumes by standing away.* Allow the liquid to evaporate completely. The white material that remains in the saucer is the pure fat (Fig. 80). It is known as cocoa butter, and it is used in making medicines such as ointments.

We Make Soap

We use soap to remove fat. Yet, soap is actually made from fat. Let's make some soap. We will work with hot fat which can be injurious unless you handle it exactly as described, so let's be careful.

We need a small pie plate and a pot cover large enough to cover the pie plate *completely.* In addition, we need a tablespoonful of washing soda and 2 tablespoons of salad oil (not mineral oil). Pour the 2 tablespoons of salad oil into the plate and add the tablespoon of washing soda. Stir the ingredients together. Place the cover over the plate and heat the mixture over a small gas flame for 15 minutes. *(Caution!* Do not uncover the plate while it is being heated or before it has completely cooled off.) Then, shut the gas and let the plate cool for 10 minutes. Examine the product. This is crude or unrefined soap. Place 1/2 teaspoon of the soap in a test tube 1/2 - full of warm water. Stopper the test tube with a cork and shake the contents vigorously for about 10 seconds. The lather that forms proves that you have made soap; however, it has not been refined, and should not be used for washing any part of the body.

Soap manufacturers make their product from fat or oil and sodium hydroxide instead of washing soda. In this process the following reaction takes place:

Glyceryl stearate (fat)	+	Sodium hydroxide (commonly called lye)	⟶	Sodium stearate (soap)	+ Glycerine

Glycerine is an important by-product in soap making. That is why soap manufacturers also sell glycerine.

The Biuret Test for Protein

The chief muscle builders in our foods are compounds called proteins. These are complicated substances, all of which contain the elements carbon, hydrogen, oxygen and nitrogen.

Let's prepare to test foods for protein (Fig. 81). You will need a medicine dropper, a glass stirring rod and several test tubes. You will also need two solutions, prepared as follows: Dissolve 1/4 teaspoon of copper sulphate in a glass of warm water. Next, prepare 1/2 glass of saturated washing soda solution. (This may easily be done by first boiling the water in a pan; turn off the gas and add as much washing soda as you can dissolve while stirring constantly with a spoon.) We are now ready to perform the test on milk, a protein-rich food.

Place a teaspoonful of milk in a test tube and add 2 teaspoons of the saturated washing soda solution. Stir the mixture with the glass rod. Add 3 drops of the copper sulfate solution with the medicine dropper (Fig. 81), and shake the test tube *once, slightly,* to cause partial mixing of the liquids. A bluish-violet color forms. This is the biuret test for protein. To test solid food for protein, first heat the food and washing soda solution in a test tube until it begins to boil; then stop heating and add the copper sulfate solution as before. Test the following for protein: uncooked white of egg, cheese, cooked fish, cooked chicken, cooked meat and apple. The result will show that only the apple did not contain protein.

99

Fig. 81. Testing for protein.

Opportunities in Biochemistry

The study of foods is part of another large branch of chemistry known as biochemistry. Medical students study biochemistry in order to understand the chemical effects of food on the human body. Your supermarket sells hundreds of food products prepared under the supervision of a biochemist who knows the nutritional value of foods and methods of preventing foods from spoiling. The biochemist is needed to make foods better, less costly and longer lasting. He has already perfected such products as quick-frozen foods, dehydrated foods, vitamin-enriched foods, vacuum-packed foods, canned foods and instant foods. All of these are the result of scientific research. We expect even greater accomplishments in the near future. Right now, scientists are working on the process of making starch and sugar from water and air! The future will certainly see wonderful things brought to us by those who study the chemistry of foods.

10 - We track down clues
with a test tube.

VISITORS from all parts of the country come to Washington
every day, to visit the famous crime detection laboratories
at the national headquarters of the F.B.I. The efficiency of
these laboratories for unravelling the flimsiest of criminal evidence is legendary. In one case, for example, the only clue
was a discarded coat with no labels or identifying marks on
it. The local police reported that the pockets were empty.
When the coat was sent to the F.B.I. they re-examined the
pockets and found a few tiny crumbs of dirt. That was enough.
The crumbs were analyzed by F.B.I. chemists who were able
to identify at least a dozen different materials used by the
suspected criminal! Among these was an unusual telltale type
of tobacco. Result: The F.B.I. found their man.

One of the important branches of chemistry is the identifica-
tion of small quantities of material. In this chapter we will
perform experiments to show how this is done.

The Flame Test

One method used to identify small quantities of material is
the *flame test*. It is based on the fact that certain elements
produce specific colors when heated in a flame. Here is an
easy way to perform the flame test.

Adjust a Bunsen burner to give a blue flame. (You may use
the flame of your kitchen stove if it burns blue.) Now sprinkle
a few grains of table salt directly on the flame. The moment
the grains of salt reach it, the flame becomes bright yellow.
This bright yellow flame will be produced not only by sodium
chloride (table salt) but by any sodium compound. You may
try sodium sulfate, sodium iodide and sodium bromide, as well
as the following sodium compounds found in the home:

Common name:	Chemical name:	Formula:
Baking soda	Sodium bicarbonate	$NaHCO_3$
Washing soda	Sodium carbonate	Na_2CO_3
Soap powder	Sodium stearate	$Na(C_{18}H_{35}O_2)$
Borax	Sodium borate	$Na_2B_4O_7$
TSP	Trisodium phosphate	Na_3PO_4

In each case, sprinkle a few grains of the substance directly on the blue flame and note the bright yellow color that forms.

The chemist, performing flame tests, uses a piece of platinum wire dipped into a solution of the compound to be tested. The wet platinum wire is then held in the blue Bunsen flame for about 10 seconds and a change in color is observed in the flame above the wire. The color lasts much longer when this method is used. If you wish to employ this technique, use a small piece of platinum wire or a piece of the less expensive nichrome wire. Before each test, wash the wire thoroughly in running water and proceed as shown in Fig. 82. Place the wire (held by tongs) in the blue flame for 10 seconds. If the wire

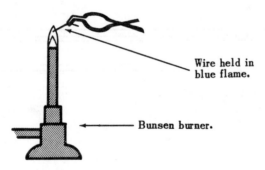

Wire held in blue flame.

Bunsen burner.

Fig. 82. Performing the flame test.

is clean, the flame will not change color. If the flame does change color, the wire must be washed again. (If the water is hard, it may be necessary to rinse the wire with distilled water.) When you are sure the wire is clean, dip it into a solution of the compound to be tested and then place the tong-held wire in the flame once again. Within 10 seconds, a change in color will be observed if any of the above compounds is used.

Do all substances turn the blue flame yellow? No! Perform the flame test with each of the following compounds shown in the left-hand column. You will produce the flame color shown in the middle column. The element in the compound that produces the flame color is shown in the right-hand column.

Compound:	Color of flame:	Color caused by:
Lithium Chloride	Crimson	Lithium
Lithium Nitrate	Crimson	Lithium
Barium Chloride	Green	Barium
Barium Nitrate	Green	Barium
Potassium Chloride	Violet	Potassium
Potassium Alum	Violet	Potassium
Strontium Chloride	Red	Strontium
Strontium Nitrate	Red	Strontium
Calcium Hydroxide*	Yellow-Orange	Calcium
Calcium Sulfate**	Yellow-Orange	Calcium

*Called slaked lime. **Sold as gypsum or Plaster of Paris in paint stores.

Now try these other compounds: Lithium sulfate, barium hydroxide, potassium sulfate and calcium chloride.

The fireworks we admire on July 4th are hardly more than firecrackers containing compounds of barium, strontium, sodium, etc. The desired color is obtained by selecting the proper element for the firecracker. When the firecracker burns, the element is heated and produces a colored flame.

One of the most valuable instruments of modern science is the spectroscope. This device analyzes the light given off by heated substances. It has been found that every element known to science produces its own peculiar kind of light. The differences in light coming from two elements are not always noticeable to the naked eye, but they can be seen with the spectroscope. Every element can be identified by means of the spectroscope.

103

The spectroscope, consequently, is the most powerful device discovered by man for analyzing chemical substances, as well as for identifying pollutants in our environment and in our food. Moreover, it is the chief tool of the astronomer in determining the chemical nature of the sun, the stars and the planets. The spectroscope will be used extensively in the SKYLAB explorations.

How to Build a Spectroscope

Commercially constructed spectroscopes are costly, but you can make one for a few cents. The most expensive item you will need is a plastic diffraction grating (obtainable from hobby shops and also from science supply houses such as Edmund Scientific Co., Barrington, N.J. 08007, for under 50 cents). Paint the inside of an ordinary shoe box black. Then, cut a one inch square hole in it, as in Fig. 83. Test the diffraction grating (Fig. 84) as follows: Hold it close to one eye and look at a bright white light for a few seconds. Then, turn your head slowly away from the light with the grating still held close to your eye. You will see a beautiful rainbow-like band of colors in which red, orange, yellow, green, blue, indigo, and violet blend into each other. This band is called a *continuous spectrum;* it is produced by separating white light into its ingredients by the diffraction grating. (If we mix red, orange, yellow, green, blue, indigo and violet *light—not paint*—we obtain white light.) By holding the grating in different positions you will see either a horizontal or a vertical spectrum. When you have found the position that produces a *horizontal* spectrum, tape the grating over the square hole as in Fig. 85.

At the opposite end of the box, cut a vertical opening one inch long and ¼-inch wide, as in Fig. 86. Tape 2 razor blades over this opening on the *inside* of the box (see Fig. 87), so that the edges of the blades are no more than 1/32nd of an inch apart. Place the cover on the box. Now, you are ready to use your spectroscope.

If you look through the grating at a bright, white light, you will see two spectra. One spectrum will appear at the side of the box, and another will appear in front of you. The latter spectrum is the one to use for your investigations.

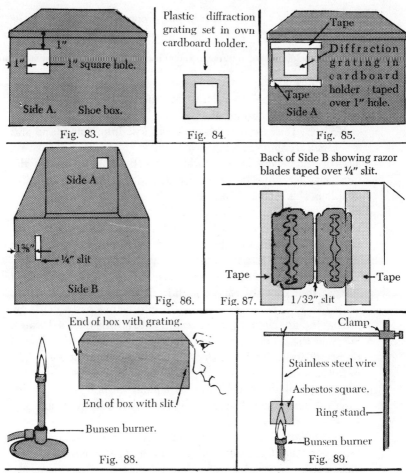

Fig. 83.

Plastic diffraction grating set in own cardboard holder.

Fig. 84.

Tape
Diffraction grating in cardboard holder taped over 1″ hole.
Tape
Side A

Fig. 85.

Side A

Side B
1⅜″
¼″ slit

Fig. 86.

Back of Side B showing razor blades taped over ¼″ slit.

Tape → ← Tape
1/32″ slit

Fig. 87.

End of box with grating.

End of box with slit.

Bunsen burner.

Fig. 88.

Clamp

Stainless steel wire

Asbestos square.

Ring stand.

Bunsen burner

Fig. 89.

For your first experiment, in a darkened room, repeat the flame test for sodium compounds described on pages 101-102. When the flame turns yellow as you sprinkle the grains of the sodium compound, hold the end of the box with the razor blade slit about five inches from the flame and look through the grating, as in Fig. 88. You will see two yellow lines. This is the *bright line spectrum* of sodium by which the chemist recognizes any substance containing sodium. Repeat the experiment with other sodium compounds.

Do the flame test with a lithium compound and examine the flame with your spectroscope. This time you will see a yellow line and a red line. With a potassium compound you will see two red lines and a violet line. There are 105 elements known to science and no two elements produce the same combination of lines. Try all of the other flame tests and keep a record of each, noting the colors and number of lines you observe.

Now, try this: Prepare a mixture of a sodium compound and a potassium compound. Perform the flame test with this mixture. The bright yellow flame produced by the sodium makes the fainter violet flame produced by the potassium completely invisible in this mixture. Examine the same flame with your spectroscope and you will see the bright line spectra of both the sodium and the potassium. The mighty spectroscope has overcome the limitations of the human eye. Experiment with other substances and make your own discoveries.

To investigate long-lasting colored flames, do the following: Take a thin sheet of asbestos and cut it into several squares, each 1″ x 1″. Then, dip one square into a thin paste made by mixing the dry chemical to be tested with a little distilled water. Suspend the asbestos square with a stainless steel wire from a ring stand as in Fig. 89. Light your burner and adjust the height of the asbestos so that the bottom of the square is just above the inner cone of the flame. (Use a separate asbestos square for each substance tested.) Your brightly colored flame should last for at least fifteen minutes.

Spectroscopy has played an important part in developing our theories of the structure of atoms and molecules. Not only does the spectroscope enable us to identify substances here on earth, but it gives us information about the chemical composition of the sun, the stars, and the planets by analyzing the light that comes from those heavenly objects.

We Make Invisible Ink

Now let's turn to a subject that has always fascinated young people – invisible ink! It has been used for centuries by spies to transmit secret information on innocent looking paper. The outbreak of World War I, in 1914, witnessed a widespread use of invisible inks (called sympathetic inks). Almost every na-

106

Fig. 90.   Milk as invisible ink.   Fig. 91.

tion had its own secret formulas which required special chemicals for detecting its invisible ink. Yet, before the war ended, no spy dared use any invisible ink. American chemists had discovered a simple process for making every sympathetic ink visible by the application of the same chemical to all invisible inks. To understand how this is possible, let's make some invisible inks and see how they become visible.

One of the oldest invisible inks is ordinary cow's milk. Select a clean pen or a fountain pen, but *do not use a ball point pen.* Pour a tablespoon of milk into a cup. If you use a fountain pen, do not fill it with any of the liquids we shall use in these experiments; simply dip the pen point into the fluid. Use the milk as if it were ink and write a message on a sheet of white paper (Fig. 90). To be sure that you have enough milk on the paper, dip the pen into the milk after each word. Then let the paper dry completely without blotting it and without using heat. You now have an invisible message on the paper.

The writing on this paper can be made visible by the use of heat. Place the paper on the rack in your kitchen oven and set at its highest temperature. Let the paper bake 5 to 10 minutes, until the entire sheet turns a very light brown. Examine the paper and the writing will be visible in dark brown lettering (Fig. 91). Why does heat make milk visible? Our next experiment will explain this.

Place a drop of milk into a clean frying pan. Put a piece of white paper, about 1-inch square, into the same pan but keep

107

it away from the milk. Now heat the pan over a large flame and see what happens. The milk boils dry and turns to a white material. This white material soon chars completely and turns dark brown. In the meantime, the paper may have just begun to char and turn slightly brown. When subjected to the same temperature, milk chars faster than paper. This enables us to see the dark brown charred milk on the light brown charred paper.

Another sympathetic ink that is developed by heat can be made by mixing 1/8 teaspoon of copper sulfate and an equal amount of ammonium chloride in half a cup of warm water.

There is a sympathetic ink which can be changed from invisible to visible and vice versa as often as you wish. This will-o'-the-wisp ink is prepared by dissolving 1/8 of a teaspoon of cobalt chloride in 1/2 cup of water. Use the ink on paper as before, and allow it to dry. Place the paper in a hot oven for about one minute and the writing appears in an attractive shade of blue. Now hold the paper, with the written side facing downward, over a pan of steaming water. The ink disappears. If you reheat the paper, the ink will reappear in blue.

Fig. 92. Starch as invisible ink.

How do we explain this? In the presence of water, cobalt chloride is an almost colorless pink which is not seen on paper.

Fig. 93.   Making starch ink visible.   Fig. 94.

When this dries, under ordinary conditions, the cobalt chloride still contains some water. When it is heated, however, all of the water is driven off and the cobalt chloride turns blue. If the cobalt chloride is then allowed to come in contact with moisture, it returns to the pale pink color.

Thus far, all of the sympathetic inks we made required heat. Other invisible inks require the use of chemicals in order to be seen. Here is an easy one to make. It is based on the reaction between starch and iodine to form a blue-black color. For this we will need paper which does not contain starch as a filler. Use the paper from a bag or part of a newspaper that has no printing. First test the paper with a drop of tincture of iodine. If the paper does not turn blue-black, it contains no starch and may be used for our experiment.

Now prepare a sympathetic ink by mixing a teaspoon of starch in 1/2 a cup of cold water. Stir until the mixture has no lumps. Write a message with the starch and water mixture (Fig. 92) and let it dry completely.

To make the writing visible we need an iodine solution, prepared by dissolving 1/2 teaspoon of tincture of iodine in 1/4 cup of water. Place the paper with the invisible message in a dish, and pour the iodine solution over it (Fig. 93). Let the paper soak in the iodine for about 15 seconds. The writing will appear in blue-black (Fig. 94).

Another sympathetic ink, depending on the use of chemicals for its detection, is made by dissolving 1/4 teaspoon of

THE INVISIBLE
COPPER SULFATE
SOLUTION
COMBINES WITH
AMMONIA VAPORS
AND APPEARS
AS A DARK BLUE
INK.

Fig. 95.   Developing and using copper sulfate ink.   Fig. 96.

copper sulfate in 1/2 a glass of water. To make the writing visible, place some ammonia water in a dish. Hold the paper, with the message side down, right over the ammonia water for about 15 seconds (Fig. 95). The writing will appear in blue (Fig. 96). Copper sulfate solution, which in this case is a very pale blue and escapes notice, combines with ammonia vapors to form a dark blue compound that is quite visible.

There are dozens of formulas for sympathetic inks, each requiring a special chemical to be made visible. Ammonia, for example, reacts with copper sulfate, but ammonia has no effect on starch. Consequently, in the past, great care was taken to keep the formula of each sympathetic ink a secret. During World War I, our chemists discovered a single master chemical which develops the writing of every invisible ink written on paper — *iodine vapor*. How does it work? It was discovered that the mere act of writing on paper disturbs the fibers of which the paper is made. Iodine vapor tends to condense on the disturbed fibers and forms a dark track. This reveals the writing regardless of the nature of the invisible ink. Does this mean that invisible inks are obsolete? No! Clever chemists will surely find an answer to the all-powerful iodine vapor.

Chromatography

Everyone has had fun mixing paints, but did you ever try to separate paints *after* they have been mixed? This may

110

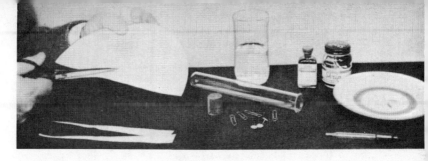

Fig. 97. Cutting strips for chromatography.

sound like a hopeless task, but it's easy if we use the method of testing by *chromatography*. Here is an experiment which illustrates the principle of this ingenious method of separating and identifying substances.

We need a 6-inch test tube and stopper to fit, filter paper, a tack, a paper clip, a *washable* blue ink (labelled washable), mercurochrome, a dish, a glass rod, and a medicine dropper. Cut the filter paper into strips (Fig. 97), 3/8 of an inch wide and at least 5 inches long. Place 2 drops of ink in the dish with the medicine dropper. Then add one drop of mercurochrome to the ink. Stir the two liquids together with the glass rod. Using the rod as a pen, and a drop of this mixture as ink, draw a thick line across a strip of filter paper at a point about 3/4 of an inch from one end of the paper (Fig. 98). The next

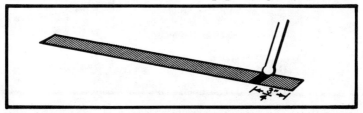

Fig. 98. Placing the mixture on filter paper.

step is to arrange the filter paper (with the dried liquid on it) in a stoppered test tube as shown in Fig. 99. Be sure to note the following:

(1) Only a small portion of the filter paper dips into the water, and the color line is *above* the water. To do this properly, it will be necessary to calculate the amount of water

111

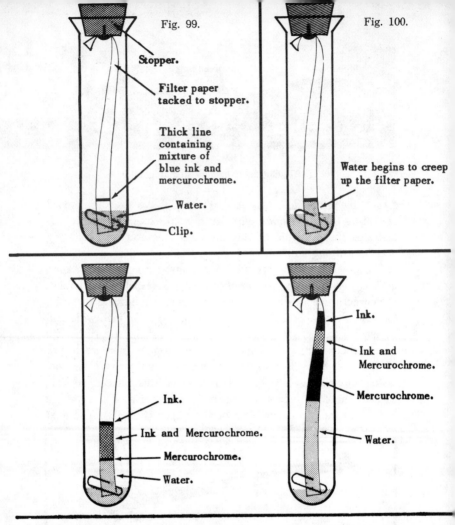

Fig. 99.

Stopper.

Filter paper
tacked to stopper.

Thick line
containing
mixture of
blue ink and
mercurochrome.

Water.

Clip.

Fig. 100.

Water begins to creep
up the filter paper.

Fig. 101.

Ink.

Ink and Mercurochrome.

Mercurochrome.

Water.

The mixture separates.

Fig. 102.

Ink.

Ink and
Mercurochrome.

Mercurochrome.

Water.

to be placed in the test tube before the filter paper is inserted.

(2) The paper clip acts as an anchor and helps keep the filter paper away from the sides of the test tube. If necessary, use a dry glass rod to push the filter paper away from the wall of the test tube.

(3) Tack the filter paper to the underside of the stopper, and keep the test tube closed.

112

(4) Place the test tube, erect, in a glass tumbler or test tube rack and watch it!

Within a few minutes you will see the water creep up the filter paper and into the spot containing ink and mercurochrome (Fig. 100). Then, as the water continues to climb, the ink and the mercurochrome accompany it, *but the ink travels faster* than the mercurochrome (Fig. 101). At the end of about 15 minutes the water will have gone a considerable distance up the paper with a band of pure blue ink right behind it (Fig. 102). Behind this will be a mixture of ink and mercurochrome. At the very end of the procession you will see a band of pure red mercurochrome.

Remove the filter paper when the ink reaches the top of the strip. You have separated the ink and the mercurochrome mixture into two distinct substances, one blue and the other red.

Chromatography is based on two factors. First, there's the attraction between the mixed substances (ink and mercurochrome), and a liquid like water. Second, there's an attraction between the mixed substances and a material like filter paper. The combination of these factors made the ink move faster than the mercurochrome.

Using the same method, separate a mixture consisting of one drop of mercurochrome and two drops of tincture of iodine, but use alcohol (rubbing alcohol) as the solvent instead of water. Again the mercurochrome travels slower and you will observe a brown band of iodine run ahead of a red band of mercurochrome. The latter becomes redder and redder as the iodine leaves it behind.

Many colored liquids are made by mixing dyes which can be separated by chromatography. Some purple inks, for example, contain a mixture of red dye and blue dye. If you have a *washable* purple ink, test it, using water as the solvent, to see if it contains more than one dye.

Some food colors are made by mixing several vegetable dyes. Buy a set of food colors in your market, and test each by chromatography, with water as the solvent. Then mix 2 or 3 dyes and separate them again by this method.

113

The chemist has devised clever methods to separate and to identify hundreds of different substances. In our experiments we have performed but a small fraction of these chemical tests. Crime detection is only one of the thousand of ways chemical tests have proven useful to us. The chemist is needed to test almost everything we use: foods, drugs, steel, paper, clothing, explosives, paint, glue, drinking water, etc., etc. Testing is part of the work of the analytical chemist who also discovers the composition and the formulas of substances. His work makes it possible to improve the materials we use, and to learn how to make them artificially from cheaper ingredients. One of the great research projects of today is the use of chromatography to discover exactly how plants make starch. When this secret is discovered, scientists will try to improve upon nature. As long as there is room for improvement in the things we need, there will be challenging opportunities for the analytical chemist.

11 - Getting inside the atom
- nuclear energy.

IN 1945 the world was astounded when a single bomb wiped out an entire city. Science had discovered a new source of immense power, *nuclear energy*. Never before had anyone liberated a force capable of such complete destruction. Many believed no good could ever come from the discovery of this terrible power. Yet, today, we see in nuclear energy the making of a better and richer world. Science is learning how to use this force to treat cancer and other ills, to improve crops, to conduct research in chemistry, biology and physics, to run ships, airplanes, trains and factories. Think of this: a piece of the element uranium, the size of a ping-pong ball, has enough nuclear energy to provide all of the United States with electrical power for an entire month. The time may come when one ounce of nuclear fuel will supply the average home with heat, light and electricity for more than 200 years.

We Look Inside the Atom

What is nuclear fuel? What is nuclear energy? To answer these questions let us go back to Chapter IV, in which an atom is described as the smallest part of an element. This means that the smallest amount of the element carbon that can exist, is an atom of carbon. Similarly, the smallest amount of the element uranium that can exist, is an atom of uranium.

Can the atom be broken up ? Yes! The atom is composed of still smaller particles called electrons, protons, and neutrons. Electrons are the same as the particles in an electric current flowing through all electrical wires. They are extremely tiny particles. Even the lightest atom, the hydrogen atom, is more than 1800 times as heavy as an electron. The proton is a much heavier particle and weighs almost as much as a hydrogen atom. It, too, is an electrical particle, but unlike the electron, it does not flow through wires.

Fig. 103.	Fig. 104.	Fig. 105.
Charging	Attracting	Attracting
a comb.	paper.	water.

Electrons, Protons and Neutrons

Electrons and protons are opposite kinds of electrical particles. Objects that attract electrons will repel (or push away) protons. To show that these are opposite kinds of particles, electrons are said to have a negative, or minus (−), electric charge; protons are said to have a positive, or plus (+), electric charge.

A neutron is composed of an electron that has united with a proton; consequently, the plus and minus charges neutralize one another and the neutron has no electric charge. An object that attracts electrons and repels protons will have no effect on neutrons.

How can we detect the attractions and repulsions of electrons and protons? Try the following experiment and see for yourself.

Rub a plastic bomb briskly (Fig. 103) for a full 30 seconds with a piece of goods made of dacron or 'nylon (an old nylon stocking will do). Rubbing causes some of the electrons in the atoms of the nylon material to be transferred to the comb. The comb now has an excess of electrons or negative charges that can attract protons in other substances. You will detect this attraction if you hold the comb very close to tiny pieces of tissue paper or newspaper. The paper is drawn up to the comb as if the latter were a magnet (Fig. 104). Repeated rubbing of the comb with nylon will increase the attraction between the comb and the paper. The excess electrons in the comb attract the protons in the atoms of the paper.

An object charged with an excess of electrons can also attract water. Adjust a faucet so that the water barely flows out

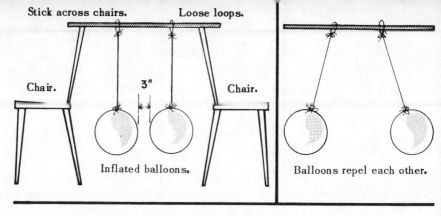

Fig. 106.   Charging and repelling balloons.   Fig. 107.

in the thinnest possible stream. Rub the comb as before, with nylon, and hold it near the top of the stream of water. The excess electrons in the comb attract the protons in the water and make the latter change its path quite noticeably (Fig. 105).

Now let us see how the particles within atoms cause repulsion, or pushing away. (Two objects having an excess of electrons will repel each other.) In our next experiment we will give 2 small balloons negative charges. In addition to the balloons we will need 2 pieces of thread about 18 inches long, a stick that is at least 2 feet long, 2 chairs, and a piece of nylon cloth.

Inflate the balloons and tie them to the stick with loose loops, as shown in Fig. 106. Support the stick at each end with a chair. Adjust the position of the loops to leave a distance of about 3 inches between the balloons when they hang freely. Without letting the balloons touch each other, rub each with the nylon cloth. Notice how the balloons push one another further apart (Fig. 107). This is repulsion caused by the negative electric charge (or excess of electrons) on each balloon.

We Make an Electroscope

You can make further studies of the actions of protons and electrons by constructing a simple electroscope as shown in Fig. 109. Use a bottle that can be fitted with a wide cork. Push a big nail with a large head through the center of the cork, leaving the head sticking out above the cork. Cut a strip

117

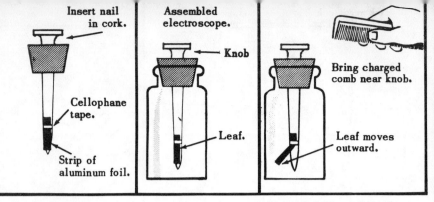

Fig. 108.   Fig. 109.   Fig. 110.

of aluminum foil, about 3 inches by 1/2 - inch, and connect it
with cellophane tape 3 inches from the sharp end of nail (see
Fig. 108). Insert the cork into the bottle, with the pointed end
of the nail and the aluminum foil hanging inside the bottle
(Fig. 109). Make sure that the end of the nail is more than
1/2 - inch from the bottom of the bottle. The foil is called
the leaf. The head of the nail above the cork is the knob. Now
try the following with your electroscope:

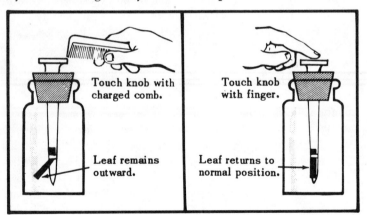

Fig. 111.   Fig. 112.

Give a plastic comb an electric charge by rubbing it with
nylon cloth. Bring the charged comb near (but not in contact
with) the knob of the electroscope (Fig. 110). As the comb
approaches the knob, the leaf moves outward. When the comb

118

is taken away, the leaf returns to its normal position. Touch the knob with the charged comb (Fig. 111), and the electroscope becomes charged; this is shown by the leaf which moves outward and *remains* that way. Touch the knob with your finger (Fig. 112) and the charge is removed; this is shown by the return of the leaf to its normal position.

In the last experiment, the electroscope had a negative charge. Some of the excess electrons in the comb were transferred to the electroscope.

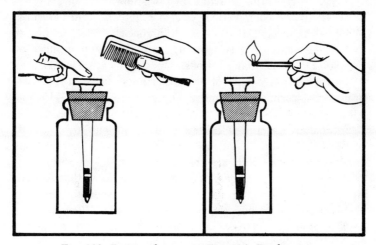

Fig. 113. Positive charge.   Fig. 114. Discharging.

To give the electroscope a positive charge, bring a freshly charged comb near the knob (but not in contact with it) and hold the comb there. Then, use your free hand to touch the knob for half a second (Fig. 113). Take your hand away from the knob and then remove the comb; the leaf will move outward as you remove the comb. The electroscope now has an excess of protons (or a positive charge). If you bring the charged comb near the knob, the leaf will return to its normal position, but it will move out again as you take the comb away. You can discharge the electroscope by holding a lit match near the knob. (Fig. 114). The flame gives off electrons which neutralize the protons in the electroscope.

119

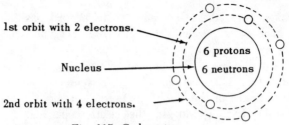

Fig. 115. Carbon atom.

The Structure of the Atom

All atoms are composed of *electrons, protons,* and *neutrons.* What, then, accounts for the difference between atoms of various elements? No two atoms have the same number of protons, electrons, and neutrons. Moreover, each element has a *different arrangement* of these particles. Look at the diagrams of a carbon atom and a uranium atom (Figs. 115 and 116).

Each atom contains a central core or nucleus in which all of the atom's protons and neutrons are located. The electrons travel in paths or orbits around the nucleus.

How is energy obtained from atoms? We know that carbon, in the form of coal, produces heat energy when it burns. In this process the carbon combines with oxygen. What happens to the protons, electrons, and neutrons when carbon atoms burn? The following change takes place:

The second orbit of electrons is given off by the carbon atom. These electrons are taken by the oxygen with which the carbon has combined. The rest of the carbon atom, especially the nucleus, is unaffected. In general, when any substance is oxidized or burned, only the outermost electrons are affected and the nucleus remains untouched. The energy we get from any ordinary fuel comes from these outermost electrons.

The nucleus of an atom, however, contains millions of times more energy than the energy of the electrons in the orbits. This energy is called *nuclear energy,* and it is not given up by the atom in the process of burning or in an other chemical reaction. How, then, is it possible to obtain energy from the nucleus of the atom?

120

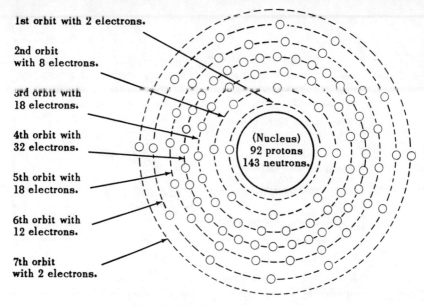

1st orbit with 2 electrons.

2nd orbit
with 8 electrons.

3rd orbit with
18 electrons.

4th orbit with
32 electrons.

5th orbit with
18 electrons.

6th orbit with
12 electrons.

7th orbit
with 2 electrons.

(Nucleus)
92 protons
143 neutrons.

Fig. 116. Uranium atom.

Radioactive Elements

A few elements do give off nuclear energy automatically. These are known as the radioactive elements; the most common ones are radium, thorium and uranium. A watch with a luminous dial contains a small amount of one of these radioactive elements. The dial shines in the dark because the nuclei of the atoms give off energy.

The following experiment, performed with a luminous watch, explains why it glows in the dark. Use a magnifying glass to examine the hands or numbers of the watch, at very close range, in a dark room. Place the watch, face upward, on a flat surface; then hold the magnifying glass next to your eye and come as close as you can to the watch, to get a clear view of the luminous paint. You will have to remain in the dark for about 5 minutes until your eyes become accustomed to the darkness. You will then be able to see tiny flashes of light coming from the luminous paint. This happens because the nuclei of radioactive atoms explode with great violence and send their particles flying out at tremendous speeds up to about 186,000 miles per second. These nuclear particles strike another chemical substance, zinc sulfide, contained in the paint. Each collision between a flying particle and a tiny zinc sulfide crystal produces a burst of light.

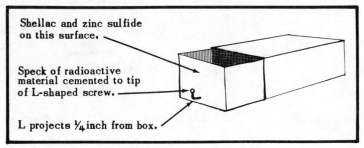

Fig. 117. Making a spinthariscope.

We Make a Spinthariscope

These bursts of light may be observed with even greater clarity by using a spinthariscope which may be obtained in most scientific supply houses. You can make your own spinthariscope from a 5-inch x 3-inch x 1 1/2 - inch cardboard match box, a magnifying glass, phosphorescent zinc sulfide a speck of radioactive material from an old luminous watch (which contains uranium, radium or thorium), shellac, and an L-shaped screw.

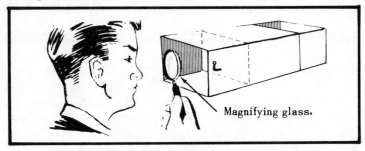

Fig. 118. Using a spinthariscope.

Cover the outer surface of one of the ends of the match box with a coat of shellac. While the shellac is wet, sprinkle a thin layer of zinc sulfide on it. After the shellac has dried, push the screw through the bottom center of the shellacked

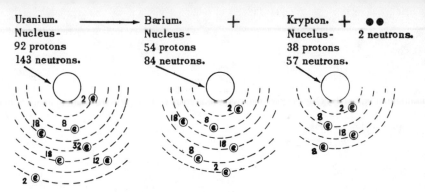

Fig. 119. Nuclear fission.

end as shown in Fig. 117. Allow the L-end of the screw to project 1/4 - inch from the box. Use tape on the inside of the box to keep the screw in place. Cement the speck of radioactive material, with a bit of shellac, to the top end of the screw. Push the shellacked end of the box containing zinc sulfide partly into the cover, and examine the zinc sulfide layer with the magnifying glass as shown in Fig. 118. Adjust the distance between the zinc sulfide surface and the magnifying glass by moving the box cover until the flashes of light are as clear as possible. A brilliant display of light will be observed when the apparatus is used in a dark room.

The light coming from the speck of radioactive material (such as uranium) in a luminous watch may not represent much energy, but if the watch you used in this experiment did contain uranium rather than radium or thorium, it can continue to produce light for billions of years to come. In fact, such a speck of uranium has already given off light for the past two billion years and its supply of energy is far from being exhausted. Just imagine what would happen if it gave all of its energy in one split second instead of spreading this process over billions of years! This is almost exactly what scientists have done.

What is Nuclear Fission?

Uranium atoms will liberate tremendous amounts of nuclear energy in a fraction of a second when they are bombarded by neutrons obtained from other atoms. The neutrons act like bullets which split the nuclei of the uranium atoms by smash-

123

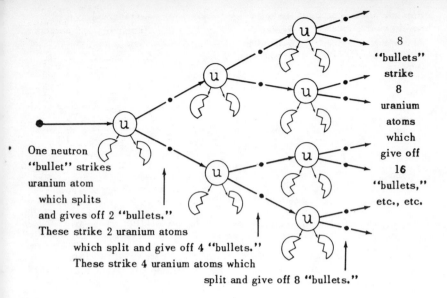

One neutron "bullet" strikes uranium atom which splits and gives off 2 "bullets." These strike 2 uranium atoms which split and give off 4 "bullets." These strike 4 uranium atoms which split and give off 8 "bullets."

8 "bullets" strike 8 uranium atoms which give off 16 "bullets," etc., etc.

Fig. 120. Chain reaction.

ing into them. Fig. 119 is an example of atom-splitting called *fission:* The uranium atom is split into smaller atoms such as barium and krypton. In addition, a few neutrons are set free. These neutrons now act as bullets and split other uranium atoms. Once the process of fission is started, it continues automatically and gains speed as shown in Fig. 120. The ever-increasing production of atomic bullets to split more and more atoms, is called a *chain reaction.*

The chain reaction leads to the rapid splitting of many uranium atoms, and liberates tremendous amounts of nuclear energy with enough power to obliterate an entire city. That is the secret of the devastating force of an atom bomb.

Energy from Nuclear Fission

How, then, can this same nuclear energy be used to run machinery? Scientists have learned how to slow down the rate at which uranium atoms are split. This is accomplished by adding the element cadmium to the uranium. When a uranium atom is split it gives off additional "bullets" in the form of neutrons, but some of these neutrons are captured when they strike cadmium atoms. Consequently, there are fewer neutrons

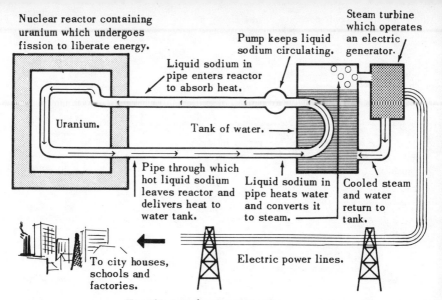

Fig. 121. A nuclear energy reactor.

to continue the splitting of other uranium atoms. Nuclear energy is given off at a slower rate. Under these conditions, there is no explosion and the nuclear energy can be used to run machinery. Fig. 121 is a schematic diagram of a nuclear energy reactor operating an electrical power plant.

How is nuclear energy used to treat cancer? We saw that the uranium atom may be split into smaller atoms such as barium and krypton. By a similar process, the splitting of uranium atoms produces other atoms such as cobalt and iodine. The atoms produced by fission continue to give off more energy by the further automatic splitting of their nuclei. Such atoms are called radioactive isotopes. The cobalt produced by the splitting of uranium is highly active. Its nucleus breaks up automatically and sends out powerful rays called gamma rays. These rays can destroy cancerous growths in the human body. Many of our hospitals now use radioactive cobalt in the treatment of cancer. In former years, radium, which also produces large amounts of gamma rays, was used in the treatment of cancer. However, radium is very costly and very few hospitals can afford to give such treatment. When scientists learned to split the uranium atom, they discovered a relatively

125

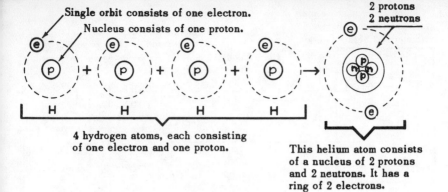

Single orbit consists of one electron.

Nucleus consists of one proton.

2 protons
2 neutrons

H   H   H   H

4 hydrogen atoms, each consisting
of one electron and one proton.

This helium atom consists
of a nucleus of 2 protons
and 2 neutrons. It has a
ring of 2 electrons.

Fig. 122. Nuclear fusion.

cheap way to make large quantities of radioactive cobalt, with its powerful gamma rays to help man in his fight against cancer.

Nuclear Fusion

Life on earth would be impossible without sunshine. Each day the sun sends us torrents of light and heat. Without the sun, the temperature on earth would drop to 459° below zero Fahrenheit. The mere thought of this is enough to make one shiver. Where does the sun get its almost endless supply of heat and light? The answer is nuclear energy.

The sun's energy is the result of a process known as *nuclear fusion*. This is the opposite of nuclear fission or splitting of nuclei. In nuclear fusion, the nuclei of very small atoms are joined together, or fused, to make a larger atom. For example, when the nuclei of four hydrogen atoms (the smallest of all atoms) are fused they form one helium atom (see Fig. 122). Nuclear fusion produces tremendous amounts of energy, far more than is produced by nuclear fission. This is the secret of the sun's great power.

Scientists have successfully imitated the remarkable process of nuclear fusion which occurs on the sun. First they asked, "What causes hydrogen atoms to fuse and form helium?" The theory was advanced that nuclear fusion takes place on the sun because of its high temperature. It was estimated that a mere 20 million degrees would be sufficient to cause nuclear fusion. Can this fantastic temperature be produced here on earth? Yes. When a uranium bomb explodes as a result of fission, a temperature over 20,000,000° Centigrade is reached. Consequently, scientists exploded a uranium bomb to obtain the temperature necessary to cause the nuclear fusion of hydrogen atoms. This led to the development of the H-bomb, or hydrogen bomb, in which a special compartment with hydrogen is placed in the center of a uranium bomb (see Fig. 123).

First, neutrons, acting as bullets, split the uranium atoms in the outer portion of the bomb. This causes an explosion by the process of nuclear fission and raises the temperature of the hydrogen compartment to more than 20 million degrees. Then, the hydrogen atoms are sufficiently hot to undergo nuclear fusion and the greatest of man-made explosions takes place. Scientists believe this gigantic force will eventually be controlled to act as another tremendous source of energy in the service of man.

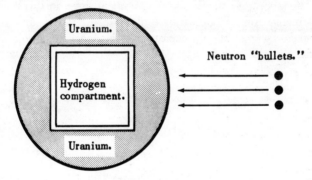

Fig. 123. The H-bomb.

The science of nuclear energy was born but a few years ago. It first found use in such devastating weapons as the A-bomb and H-bomb. Even more important for human welfare are the many applications of nuclear energy as a soucrce of power for the machines of industry, for transportation, and for our homes. It has begun to achieve wonders in medicine and in the research laboratories of chemistry, physics and biology. The nuclear scientist of tomorrow may well hold the future of the world in his hands.

How to Keep Records

The scientist keeps an accurate account of his experiments. His laboratory note book is invaluable for keeping a record of his actual experiments. You might keep your own records in any large-sized note book. Arrange your notes as shown in the following sample experiment:

Date:

Purpose: To test bicarbonate of soda for sodium.

Method: I dissolved some bicarbonate of soda in a little water. Then I dipped a nichrome wire into the solution and placed the wire in a blue Bunsen flame.

Observation: The flame turned yellow.

Conclusion: Since all sodium compounds turn the blue flame yellow, bicarbonate of soda contains sodium.

Sources of Chemical Supplies

The laboratory supplies and equipment listed in this book are obtainable from laboratory supply houses, model and hobby shops, or science supply departments of department stores near you.